COMPUTERS AND SOCIETY

McGRAW-HILL COMPUTER SCIENCE SERIES

RICHARD W. HAMMING
Bell Telephone Laboratories, Incorporated

EDWARD A. FEIGENBAUM
Stanford University

COMPUTERS AND SOCIETY

R. W. HAMMING

Bell Telephone Laboratories, Incorporated
Murray Hill, New Jersey

Adjunct Professor
Department of Computer Sciences
The City College of New York

McGraw-Hill Book Company

New York, St. Louis, San Francisco, Düsseldorf, Johannesburg,
Kuala Lumpur, London, Mexico, Montreal, New Delhi,
Panama, Rio de Janeiro, Singapore, Sydney, Toronto

COMPUTERS AND SOCIETY

Library of Congress Catalog Card Number 77-159306
07-028593-7
345678910 MUMU 76543

This book was set in Journal Roman by Creative Book Services, division of McGregor & Werner, Incorporated, and printed on permanent paper and bound by Vail-Ballou Press, Inc. The designer was Creative Book Services, division of McGregor & Werner, Incorporated. The editors were Richard F. Dojny and Hiag Akmakjian. Sally Ellyson supervised production.

Contents

Preface

The purpose of this book is to present many of the ideas involving the digital computer and its relation to modern society. The presentation is designed for liberal arts and humanities-oriented people who wish to know about computers without learning to run them. Just as in music appreciation courses where the student is allowed to hear music before he can read notes or play an instrument, so too it seems possible to learn a great deal about computers and their role in our society without at the same time learning to use them. Learning to run a computer would, of course, add a lot, but, considering the amount of effort involved in mastering even the simplest computers, it is very doubtful that the time spent in mastering the mechanics of currently available machines with their currently available software (in the form of both a language and an operating system) is worth the results. The chief result of such an approach tends to be a very myopic view of computers and their importance. Instead of discussing how to program a particular machine, or use a particular language and operating system, this book concentrates on ideas and aspects of computers that seem to have more than transitory importance, though of course no claim is made of perfect selection.

It is difficult to communicate abstract ideas. If the idea is presented first, then a large halo of vagueness surrounds the whole until it is illustrated by concrete examples—which are promptly seized upon as being the idea. The reverse presentation, giving the particular examples first and then trying to develop the idea from them, has its corresponding faults. Thus, while concentrating on the ideas surrounding the digital computer and its use, we will try to make the ideas concrete by including some details, but at the same time we will try to prevent the specific details of how current machines are built and used from obscuring the basic ideas.

Many books on the applications of digital computers list examples under the headings of the fields of applications. Instead of this approach, which again has the air of being a matter of current chance so far as basic concepts are concerned, we have chosen to present the applications arranged around central ideas, regardless of the field to which they apply. Instead of chapter headings of, say, medical, legal, engineering, linguistic, and social applications, we have chosen such abstract ideas as modeling, feedback, stability, randomness, analog-to-digital conversion, and optimization. There is no certainty that this approach will be relevant to the world of the future, but it seems to have a greater survival value than the usual presentations.

The notes for the book have gone through several drafts that were used to teach a course and the final form is based on this experience. My thanks are due to the many students, friends and colleagues, as well as my management, who have made this book possible.

R. W. Hamming

A Note on the Photographs

Ever since man began to count he has been intrigued by the possibility of computing easily, rapidly, and—particularly in some of the more abstract parts of science, where solutions are not empirically verifiable—with ever-increasing accuracy. Although most historians assumed that ancient Greek technology was not as advanced as its theoretical knowledge, in 1900 Greek sponge fishermen found a clockwork mechanism that had been lying on the bottom of the Aegean Sea for 2,000 years, attesting to considerably more knowledge on the part of the Ancients than had been believed (see page 1).

Starting in the Near East about 5,000 years ago, and spreading through most of the Eastern Hemisphere, the abacus was used for arithmetic calculations. Some abacus operators are so adept that, even today, they can compute faster than many desk adding machines (page 19).

Calculations were felt to be needed in other areas of inquiry—for example, in measuring the movements of heavenly bodies in the solar system. In Jaipur, India, an astronomy laboratory was built on a monumental scale to measure and compute the course of stars, planets, sun, and moon (page 41). Its accuracy was impressive. For centuries there were few further developments in mechanical computation, even though mathematics continued to evolve in Europe and North Africa.

Then, beginning about 350 years ago, calculating devices of varying inventiveness began to appear. In 1617 Baron von Napier invented a small, simple device (carved out of ivory, hence nicknamed "Napier's bones") made of rods bearing digits 1 to 9, with their multiples under them. To multiply two numbers the rods were rotated so that the answer was found by adding numbers in horizontally adjacent squares (page 65). In 1623, Professor Wilhelm Schickard of

Tübingen devised a calculating machine (page 87), which he described in a letter to the astronomer Johannes Kepler. It was more sophisticated than the more famous adding machine of Blaise Pascal, invented in 1642 when he was 19, because Pascal was tired of doing the arithmetic for his tax-collector father (page 109).

In 1671, the great German philosopher and mathematician Gottfried Leibniz turned his efforts to building a calculator. He produced one which could multiply, divide, and extract roots, as well as add and subtract (page 125). It was only a few years later that he independently discovered the differential and integral calculus.

In the nineteenth century, Charles Babbage, an English inventor, constructed an engine of toothed wheels on shafts to calculate and print mathematical tables. Its failure was due to an irrelevant cause: the working parts could not be tooled to precision by the technology of his day.

The relatively slow pace of development in the past twenty centuries has accelerated rapidly in the past 40 years. Beginning with devices such as the Complex Computer (page 171) by G. R. Stibitz, a Bell Telephone Laboratories research mathematician, the age of computers began, and in earnest. In rapid succession the IBM Corporation and other manufacturers developed increasingly more sophisticated, sensitive, and complex devices, using the most technologically advanced knowledge. The IBM 601 Automatic Multiplier (page 195), the Mark I Relay Computer (page 213), the IBM 603 Electronic Multiplier (page 229), the IBM 702 Electronic Data Processing Machine (page 247), and most recently, the IBM System 370 (page 263) made computation extraordinarily easy. The IBM System 370 performs arithmetic and logical operations at speeds measured in billionths of a second, with a capacity of 800 million characters of data, printing out 2,000 lines a minute, a reflection of the evolving interrelation of man's scientific needs and his computational abilities. Through this varying development over two millennia the impetus has been a constant one: the increase in knowledge has advanced technique, which has in turn still further increased knowledge.

COMPUTERS AND SOCIETY

CHAPTER 1

Greek Clockwork Mechanism (65 B.C.)
Courtesy of D. J. de Solla Price.

1

Introduction to Computers

THE COMPUTER AS A TOOL   1.1

It has often been said that man is the tool-making animal. Other animals do make a few tools, but man is *the* tool-making animal. For example, man made a hammer to increase his muscle power, a microscope to increase the range of his vision, and an oscilloscope to give him the new sense to detect small electric currents. It is easy to give many more examples of tools man has made, from chisels and motors to telephones and airplanes.

Man also invented language. Language is a tool, but it is a tool for the mind rather than the body. An argument could be made that language arose as a means for organizing and coordinating the body efforts of a group of people, but even though this may be true, the use of language now transcends so limited a view. Indeed, the invention of language has given rise to poetry and literature, both of which are more concerned with pleasure than with engineering efficiency.

At first glance, the computing machine appears to be just another tool to aid the body—to carry out long, tedious, exacting sequences of arithmetic operations. But many years of experience reveals that, like languages, *computers are more tools to aid the mind than they are tools to aid the body.* A great deal of this book is devoted to illustrating and justifying this opinion.

When you consider how difficult it is to explain both the value and use of the invention of language, it should become apparent why the corresponding explanations for computers will not be easy, and why much of the book is devoted to these points.

LANGUAGE   1.2

The so-called natural languages, both written and spoken, are what usually first come to mind when the word *language* is used. A little thought, however, brings the realization that there are other widely used languages, mathematics being one of the most useful ones in modern science. Other examples of languages are musical notation and the language of maps.

Perhaps the most distinguishing feature of natural languages is that they can be processed in a linear sequence in time.[1] That is, we hear or read the words one after another—though at times we work with larger or smaller units than words. In the language called *mathematics* there can be difficulty in trying to use a strictly sequential scan of an equation or formula to grasp the total meaning of what is written. We do indeed scan a complex mathematical formula, but we must frequently search back and forth for the *pattern* of the symbols and how they are interrelated if we are to grasp the meaning of what is written. It is often difficult, therefore, to read aloud complicated mathematical expressions in any satisfactory manner. The extreme example of a commonly used nonsequential language is that of maps, especially road maps. One can tell a friend over a telephone which routes to follow, but that is not the same as describing the whole map. With sufficient effort a map can be transmitted from one person to another over a telephone, but it is often surprisingly difficult to do it accurately and reliably.

Large-scale digital computing machines operate in an essentially sequential manner, and they are best applied to those situations that can be reduced to a sequence of operations. That is not to say that some apparently nonsequential problems cannot be handled, but only

---

[1] Marshall McLuhan makes a great point of this readily observed fact.

that the machines, being fundamentally sequential, have had their greatest successes on sequential problems.

There are a number of other important ways in which computing machines are related to language. First, it should be obvious that if we are to use a computer, we must be able to communicate with it in some mutually understood language. The above sentence was deliberately phrased to mean—as we shall later show—that we do not have to use any one particular language. We are free to design our own language of communication with the machine, *provided* we can also give specific, detailed rules for translation from our newly designed language to the machine language that the engineers have built into the particular computer we are using.

We shall also look at a number of applications of computers to questions that arise in the field of language. Because we have already designed a large number of artificial languages to make communication with computers easy for humans, we have had to face a number of new and interesting engineering-type questions involving how to do it practically and with reasonable efficiency. Such questions did not arise in the classical descriptive approach to language. Language, being the result of long evolution, is presumably well-adapted to do what it does. Our difficulty is that we do not actually understand language and what it does and how it does it. Our new engineering approach asks new questions that are different from those asked in classical linguistics, and hence the answers are also new. It is widely recognized that progress in a field is often greatest when there is a change in the kinds of questions asked.

In summary, computers have many different relationships with language, and may, in some respects, be considered as an invention comparable in importance to the invention of language. Certainly their use has forced us to reexamine carefully how a language is used as a method of communication.

THE COMPUTER REVOLUTION   1.3

It has become common to compare the current Computer (or Control) Revolution with the Industrial Revolution. The Industrial Revolution freed man from being a beast of burden living essentially by his muscle power. The Computer Revolution promises to free man from simple, repetitive actions based on learned responses—"conditioned responses," as psychologists call them.

The invention of the steam engine was the heart of the Industrial Revolution. It was the source of mechanical power. There had been waterwheels and windmills before, but the steam engine provided the first powerful, flexible, reliable source of power. In order to use the steam engine it was necessary to invent or adapt various such other machines as the spinning jenny, the steam locomotive, the steamship, the lathe, and so on, to make use of the power.

The invention of the digital computer is at the heart of the Computer Revolution. It is the source of computing power, the power to process information. In order to use this power we must "invent" the applications, we must say how and to what this power is to be applied. That is, we must write programs for the computer describing each new application.

The early steam engines produced tens of horsepower, hardly a hundredfold increase over man or animal power, while in less than 20 years digital computers have been developed to where they have more than a millionfold the power of a human with a mechanical desk calculator. It is rare for anyone to see a million horsepower operating for any length of time. On the other hand, a million human power in computing is a common sight in computing installations. We will later say more about the significance of such a great increase in power. In both cases, to some extent, the invention and practical development of the source of power was the catalytic agent that precipitated the many subsequent events.

The Industrial Revolution produced profound changes in the structure of our society and in the patterns of life for the individual. These changes were accompanied by some necessary and much unnecessary suffering and dislocation of people from their accustomed ways of life. The Computer Revolution threatens to cause similar hardships, but there are reasons to believe we may now be wise enough to get through the transition stages with much less human suffering, though of course there will be changes. Change does not necessarily mean progress, but progress requires change.

The analogy of the Computer Revolution to the Industrial Revolution is, however, not exact. The Industrial Revolution drove Western man away from living primarily by his brawn into the area of using the higher abilities of his central nervous system. The Computer Revolution

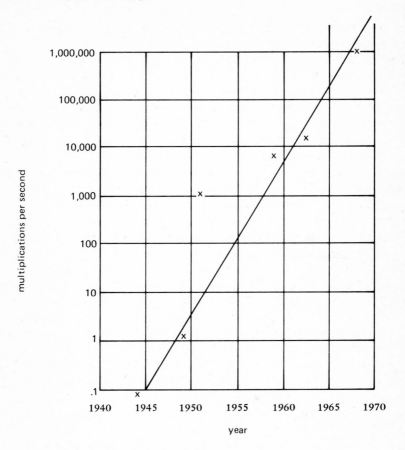

Figure 1-1 Typical machine speeds as a function of time.

is driving him out of part of this area, and there appears to be no comparable area to retreat to except to the higher and higher uses of his central nervous system. Furthermore, the Computer Revolution is apparently proceeding much more rapidly than did the Industrial Revolution and hence presents its new problems at a far more rapid pace.

Statistics about the Computer

Large-scale digital computers have many different properties and cannot be completely summarized briefly, but they are traditionally measured by two features: how much information they can store, and

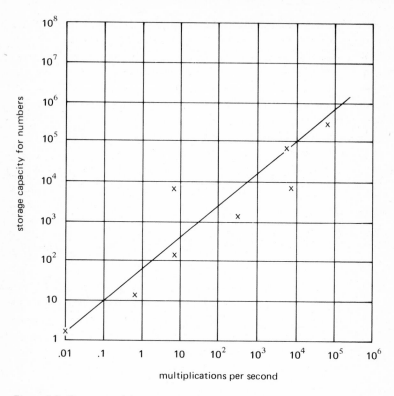

Figure 1-2 Storage capacity versus speed.

how fast they can perform the four basic operations of arithmetic, addition, subtraction, multiplication, and division. Of these four operations, speed of multiplication is the usual guide to how fast a machine is, though in many applications other measures of its speed are far more appropriate.

Currently available (1970) machines can do the equivalent of 8 to 12 decimal-digit multiplications at a rate of more than a million per second and a few in the tens of millions. Thus, some computing machines are almost 100 million times faster than hand calculation (even when aided by a desk calculator).

Figure 1-1 shows some typical machine speeds as a function of time. Note that the vertical axis gives, for equal spaces, equal multiplicative factors in operations per second (that is, we have plotted the log of the operations per second). This is a common way of representing information that changes greatly over the range of interest. The advantage is that it represents the *percentage change* very clearly, rather than the absolute change, and in rapidly growing situations it is usually the percentage change that matters most. For example, we are more concerned with the rate of growth of the Gross National Product (GNP) then we are with the actual increases themselves.

Speed and the capacity to store information in a computer are typically related because we seldom perform millions of operations on only a few numbers or items of information. Figure 1-2 shows the relationship of the speed and storage capacity for a number of machines. This time we have used equal increments on *both* axes of the figure to represent equal multiplicative factors (logs).

Since it is difficult to comprehend what a change by a factor of a million means, we shall give a few simple examples. Change is often measured in *orders of* magnitude (see Table 1.3-1).

Table 1.3-1

orders of magnitude	=	*a factor of*
1		10
2		$100 = 10^2$
3		$1,000 = 10^3$
4		$10,000 = 10^4$
5		$100,000 = 10^5$
6		$1,000,000 = 10^6$

Humans can walk, normally, at around 4 miles per hour. They drive their cars at about 40 miles per hour, a one order of magnitude increase in speed. Yet cars by their speed alone have produced fundamental changes in our way of life. Jet planes (1970) typically fly at speeds of 400 to 600 miles per hour, slightly more than two orders of magnitude faster than walking, and in their turn have changed many patterns of life, letting us now fly to places where it would take too long to drive, let alone walk. Space vehicles go at speeds less than four orders of magnitude greater than walking. Computers, on the other hand, are a full seven orders of magnitude faster than hand computation, and we confidently expect that in the near future large-scale integrated circuit technology will produce further increases in speed. However, according to the theory of relativity there is a maximum velocity at which we can signal, namely, the velocity of light. It is believed that no practical signalling system can signal faster than this. If we make the components of the computer smaller then we can pack them closer together so that it takes less elapsed time for the signal to go from one component to the next. We cannot indefinitely shrink the size of the components because we are limited by the size of the molecules we use to make the components. Thus it appears that there are very definite limits, though they are still far away, beyond which we cannot hope to go. At the moment it appears that getting rid of the heat that computing generates may be the limit, rather than the velocity of light.

A second analogy may help dramatize the meaning of a change by a factor of a million. Consider these two different situations. In the first, all the money you have in the world is $1, and in the second you have $1,000,000. The differences in the way you look at the world in the two situations are very great indeed. In one case your horizons are very strictly limited, while in the other there is the problem of how to choose among the many things you might do.

Still using dollars as a basis for measuring, the computer industry grew from practically nothing in 1948 to over $6.5 billion annually in 1968. On the other hand, the cost per basic operation has decreased by almost a factor of 10,000. If automobile prices dropped that much you would frequently not bother to park a car: you could throw it away and buy a new one when you needed it! Thus, much that was prohibitively expensive when we had only hand methods is now done routinely. Indeed, most of what we now do on computers we could not and would not have done by hand.

At present (1970) there are around 60,000 computers installed in the United States, and the rate of growth of installations is still not falling off.

COMMENTS ON THE HISTORY OF TECHNOLOGY   1.4

It is natural to look for the early development of computing and computing machines in the early history of mathematics. Perhaps the one-to-one correspondence between objects and the digits could be called the first primitive step in computing. The Greek writer Herodotus (484-425 B.C.) attributed the rise of geometry to the Egyptians' need to resurvey their lands every year after the Nile flood to determine the taxes to be levied. "From this practice, I think, geometry first came to be known in Egypt, whence it passed into Greece."[2] Furthermore, it is often claimed that arithmetic arose out of the practical needs of the very mercantile-oriented Babylonians.

The theory that mathematics resulted from the practical needs of the people is very plausible. But it is at least, if not more, plausible to suspect that mathematics arose out of the artistic or religious needs of men. Any good mathematician will tell you (usually at great length) of the importance of aesthetics in current mathematics, and Aristotle observed, "Thus the mathematical sciences originated in the neighborhood of Egypt, because there a priestly class was allowed leisure."[3] It has often been claimed that all progress is due to lazy men. An examination of some of the problems in the earliest mathematical records yet found, the Rhind Mathematical Papyrus, the Moscow Papyrus, and the Mathematical Cuneiform Texts,[4] shows that even then the problems given to students were no more practical than those given today, and perhaps even less so! Rather than supposing that geometry arose out of the need for surveying, one can equally well imagine that it arose out of the need to fit geometric patterns into the human face and body in preparation for dances and religious rites,[5] and that advanced counting and arithmetic arose out of the "magic properties" of numbers that still amuse us to this day.

Records that have come down to us from the far distant past show how skillful our ancestors were. For example, consider the cave paintings remaining from early civilization. Paolo Graziosi in *Paleolithic Art* (26,000 to 10,000 B.C.) says, "Undoubtedly the most perplexing aspect of the art phenomenon when it appears to us for the first time, is the high degree of maturity shown in the earliest expressions. The

[2] *The History of Herodotus,* Book II.

[3] B. L. Van Der Waerden, *Science Awakening,* P. Noorhoff Ltd., Groningen, Holland, 1954.

[4] H. O. Midonick, *The Treasury of Mathematics,* Philosophical Library, New York, 1965.

[5] A. Seidenberg, "The Ritual Origin of Geometry," *Archive for History of Exact Science*, vol. I, 1962, pp. 488-527, and "The Ritual Origin of Counting," ibid., pp. 1-40.

sudden appearance of stylistically evolved works of art takes us completely by surprise. . . ." Later he observes, "All this leads us to assume the existence, at that time, of proper art schools which led to the creation and improvement of techniques, and handed down to subsequent generations the knowledge and skill achieved through the centuries."[6] Anyone who looks at even reproductions of cave paintings will soon realize that they were not the chance productions of talented amateurs. Correspondingly, Stonehenge (I: 1900-1700 B.C.; II: 1700-1500 B.C.; III: 1500-1400 B.C.) and other megalithic structures seem to reveal very great mathematical, astronomical, and engineering skills.[7,8]

Thus, we can only speculate about the earliest history of computing and computing machines since they clearly appeared far in prehistory. A number of indisputable technical facts that we have from the past suggest a degree of sophistication that is at variance with the more traditional view of history. It is apparently customary for historians when looking at engineering achievements in the past, including the great Roman aqueducts and roads, the Gothic cathedrals and even the pyramids, to try to guess how little technical knowledge might have been used rather than to try to estimate the probable amount that was available. They are reluctant to admit that our ancestors were remarkably able men with deep insight into the nature of the world.

Of the two extreme theories offered above, the utilitarian and the aesthetic, probably both are wrong, and the truth lies somewhere in between, with more emphasis than is usually recognized on the artistic side.

Early Computing Machines

It is plausible that both pebbles and marks would have been used as elementary computing devices, and that the abacus evolved out of the systematic use of pebbles in pot holes.

In 1900 Greek sponge divers found, just off the Aegean island of Antikythera, an elaborate clockwork mechanism having at least twenty

[6] McGraw-Hill Book Company, New York, 1960.

[7] R. J. C. Atkinson, *Stonehenge*, Hamish Hamilton, London, 1956.

[8] G. S. Hawkins, *Stonehenge Decoded*, Doubleday & Co., Garden City, N.Y., 1965.

geared wheels still intact.[9] This is at present our earliest surviving mechanism of such complexity, and although we are not certain, it was apparently used for navigation. Its well attested age (65 B.C., plus or minus 10 years), shows how faulty our traditional records and accounts of the classical Greek civilization are when they do not include references to such elaborate computing mechanisms. Almost all of early Greek history has come down to us via literary channels, written by the literary people in classical Greece. Consider the future historians' troubles if the only records they have of our civilization are those written by novelists, playwrights, and poets, and how badly they will reconstruct our highly technical age. Furthermore, the scanty records from Greece were filtered both by what the literary people of the Middle Ages could understand and by what they thought worthy of preservation. As a result we are left in almost complete darkness as to the true history and development of early computing machines.

One of the earliest reliably recorded computing devices is that of the Baron von Napier (1550-1617) who developed logarithms, and a set of ivory rods, sometimes called "Napier's bones," that aid in doing multiplications.

An interesting letter dated December 20, 1623 has recently been found. It is from Wilhelm Schikard, Professor of Mathematics and Astronomy, University of Tübingen near Stuttgart,[10] to Kepler (1571-1630), formulator of Kepler's laws concerning the motions of the planets about the sun. In the letter Schickard apologizes for the fact that the model of a computing machine that he was building for Kepler has burned up. This note has only recently been discovered and has not yet been followed up, but apparently the machine could do not only additions and subtractions, but also multiplications and divisions.

It is traditionally noted that the first mechanical computing machine was built by Blaise Pascal (1623-1662), author of the *Provincial Letters* and the famous mathematician, who as a child helped his father with the town tax collection records. This machine could do only additions and subtractions.

The famous Gottfried Leibniz (1646-1716), mathematician, phi-

---

[9] Derek J. de Solla Price, *Science Since Babylon*, Yale University Press, New Haven, 1961.

[10] V. Capla, *Stroje Na Zpraeovani Informati*, **110**, 1946, pp. 321-325.

losopher, historian, politician, statesman, etc., is often credited with building the first multiplying device. However, it was never very reliable.

Charles Babbage (1791-1871)[11,12] is generally credited with being the first to grasp the general concept of a modern computing machine. He had started to build a simple "difference engine" to compute tables (using the first six differences of the numerical entries to develop a table), when he realized that a far more ambitious machine could not only do the arithmetic involved, but could also direct itself from step to step, choosing the next step contingent upon the results just obtained, or obtained at some earlier time. He was associated with Lady Lovelace, Lord Byron's daughter, and she left some records that indicate that she was the world's first programmer who understood the power of a computing machine. Unfortunately, despite some government support, Babbage did not complete any of his machines.

In September 1940 George Stibitz of the Bell Telephone Laboratories[13] exhibited a simple relay computing machine at the American Mathematical Society's annual meeting at Dartmouth, in Hanover, New Hampshire. The terminal was there, while the main computing unit of the machine was in New York City, and the two were connected with (slightly adjusted) telephone lines. Thus, the currently glamorous *remote console* type of computing is quite old.

Stibitz continued to develop his ideas in a sequence of machines. The Model 5, of which two were built for the United States government, had floating-point arithmetic, a feature that was not produced again for some years. Stibitz also suggested the use of the binary system of representing information.

From 1935 onward, IBM manufactured a multiplying punch, the IBM 601, that was widely used in commercial work and proved to be vital to much of the earliest scientific work done using machines, including the design of the atomic bomb at Los Alamos. In all they

[11] M. Mosley, *Irascible Genius,* Hutchinson, London, 1964.
[12] P. & E. Morrison, *Charles Babbage and His Calculating Engines,* Dover Publishers, New York, 1961.
[13] G. R. Stibitz and Mrs. E. Loveday, "The Relay Computers at Bell Laboratories," *Datamation,* April and May 1967.

made about 1,500 such machines. They differed in some details; for example, some had a division feature and the possibility of forming a triple product A × B × C.

Before and during World War II, Konrad Zuse[14] of Germany also developed several practical computing machines. In 1944, Howard Aiken at Harvard, with aid from IBM, built one of the more famous computers, the Mark I Relay Computer.

During World War II, Mauchly and Eckert developed the first completely electronic computing machine, the ENIAC, under a government contract. The machine was originally designed to compute ballistic tables (as were several of Stibitz's early machines) for the Aberdeen Proving Grounds. It was a great step forward in speed, being capable of about 10,000 operations per second.

As is so often the case, hardly was the ENIAC built when new ideas occurred to the designers. Von Neumann of the Institute for Advanced Study recognized the importance of the idea of *internal programming*. Internal programming means that instructions can be stored internally, just as the numbers are, and that the machine itself can change its own instructions. The idea was developed it in a series of famous reports. As a result of a course on computers in the summer of 1946 given by Mauchly and Eckert, and of the Institute reports, many different groups started to build computers of more or less the same design, and the EDSAC, built by M. V. Wilkes in Cambridge, England, had the honor of being the first one to actually work. The SEAC at the Bureau of Standards was a close second, and it probably did more useful work than any other early machine.

From there on the history of computing machines is that of many active university groups, and then gradually commercial manufacturers, building machines.

Electronic computers are sometimes classified into three generations, the first based on vacuum tubes, the second on transistors, and the third on integrated circuits. This evolution has produced enormous increases in speed and reliability and a corresponding decrease in cost per operation done. More is to be expected before the evolution ends.

---

[14] He was honored along with Stibitz by a prize from the AFIPS.

CHANGES IN SCIENCE   1.5

Computers have had a great effect in the field of science, so much so that they have significantly changed how science is done. At one time most experiments were done in a laboratory and only a few were conducted by making computations from known theory. By 1970, probably 80 to 90 percent of the experiments in many fields were done on a computing machine and only occasionally, often only after many computer runs, was an experiment itself done in the laboratory. The reasons for this are that using the computing approach is simpler, faster, and cheaper than most laboratory work, and often more enlightening. Of course, the possibility of doing an experiment on a computing machine depends upon having an adequate theory available, and we are gradually building up such theories in many fields.

Another readily observed effect of computers on science is the reduction of the amount of laboratory space relative to office space in the typical research center or university. What is already true in the physical sciences will soon be true in the social sciences where experimentation with humans is not only expensive but often unethical. Many of the social sciences have no choice but to simulate experiments using computers as their basic research tool.

The effects of computers on science are only beginning, and, as we shall see later, there are many aspects yet to be exploited.

COMPUTERS AND BUSINESS   1.6

Business took to computing machines somewhat earlier but more slowly than did science. Thus, the IBM 601 was designed for business applications, and it was only with some real difficulties that it was adapted to scientific work. But until now (1970) the range of applications of the modern electronic machines to science has exceeded that of business, probably both because the designers tended naturally to be scientists and to favor scientifically-oriented machines, and because of the natural conservatism and lack of imagination (plus a justified fear of getting a faulty machine and losing a lot of money) on the part of the commercial interests. However, commercial applications beyond plain accounting are slowly coming into their own and are now influencing computer design because, if for no other reason, business represents so large a dollar part of the market. Business is slowly beginning to use this new powerful tool in imaginative ways.

APPLICATIONS OF COMPUTERS 1.7

It would be tedious as well as rather uninformative to list all the applications of computers. Many of them are well known to any reasonably alert person. Thus, computers are not only featured on election nights but used for college registration, airline reservations, space shots, checking income tax returns, census data reduction, most of science, business billing, bank checks, inventory planning, genealogical studies, many toll roads, highway traffic control, determining authorship of disputed documents, and so on.

Computers reach into, and affect directly as well as indirectly, many aspects of human life, and in the future they promise (threaten) to invade even more. One of the main purposes of this book is to give the reader some grasp on how to cope with this invasion, how to guide it rather than oppose it and then be forced to take the consequences of directly opposing the inevitable. It is *not* foreordained that computers shall make the world a hideous place to live. Computers are very flexible and can be used in many positive ways. For example, in place of mass production of the same identical product over and over again, they give the possibility of *the mass production of a variable product,* each one made to fit a particular consumer's desires and whims. If people make it clear that they want variety rather than stereotyped monotony and are also willing to pay a modest amount for variety, then they will have that variety. Otherwise, society will probably follow the path of least resistance and maximum short-term profit and try to make everyone conform to the easiest way of running the machines. The evil or good does not rest in the computer, it rests with the user. And if people demand that computers be used in ways to make life more pleasant than it is at present, then computers will be so used—but not unless people demand it. That is the way democracy works.

There is a simple and natural test to apply to any new application of computers which interacts with humans and that is this: *does the human have more or fewer options (freedom) now than he had before the use of the computer?*

If most applications increase the choices a human has, then we shall gradually create a world of great freedom. And if it goes the other way, then we shall create a hell for ourselves. The evil is not in the tool, it is in the way it is used.

Some words of modification are needed in practice. Many times the application of a computer requires (practically) the changing of the choices available to the human, so that exactly the same choice cannot be maintained. However, the new choices should be meaningful, not empty. Lastly, they should be described in a form easy for the human to use and understand.

As a simple example, the handling of student registration on machines should not remove the student's freedom to select his quiz section.

It is true, of course, that using the machine to increase the options of people will often be at the expense of machine efficiency. But who is to be the master, man or the machine? There are times—many times—when humane living should take precedence over mere efficient living.

CHAPTER **2**

Abacus
From an original in the IBM Corporation Antique Calculator Collection.

2

Representation of Information

The previous chapter observed that the digital computer provides the power to process information. In this chapter we shall investigate how we represent information so that a computer can process it. In the next chapter we will investigate how we can represent the processes to be performed on the information, and in Chapter 4 we will examine the digital computer that actually does the processing of the information. Chapters 5 and 6 will show a number of examples of how the three parts, the information, the process, and the machine, are put together to solve specific problems.

THE BINARY SYSTEM FOR REPRESENTING
INFORMATION   2.1

If we are to develop a theory of how to handle information, we will need a notation for representing information as well as a computer for handling and transforming it. The most common devices for representing information are *two-state* devices such as a relay that may be open or closed, a position on a paper tape or card that may or may not be punched with a hole, a spot on a magnetic tape that is magnetized either North-South or South-North, a magnetic core that is magnetized either of two ways, a two-state "flip-flop circuit" of transistors (or vacuum tubes), or a wall switch for controlling an electric light in a home. It is convenient to have an abstract method for symbolizing the two alternative states without reference to the particular device that is being used. The most common way is to use the symbol 0 for one state and the symbol 1 for the other state, though any two differing marks could be used. This method of using two states is called *the binary system for the representation of information,* and at the moment we regard the 0 and 1 as merely arbitrary marks having no relation to numbers.

By combining several binary symbols we can represent more than two states. Thus two binary symbols side by side can represent $2 \times 2 = 4$ states; the states may be represented by

00   01   10   11

Three binary symbols can represent $2 \times 2 \times 2 = 8$ states; they are

000   001   010   011   100   101   110   111

In general, n binary symbols can represent $2 \times 2 \times 2 \dots \times 2 = 2^n$ states. A table of powers of 2 (Table 2.1-1) shows how rapidly such a system grows in capacity as n increases.

Table 2.1-1

$2^1 = 2$	$2^{10} = 1,024$
$2^2 = 4$	$2^{20} = 1,048,576$
$2^3 = 8$	$2^{30} = 1,073,741,824$
$2^4 = 16$	$2^{40} = 1,099,511,627,776$
$2^5 = 32$	etc.

For convenience, a single binary digit is often called a *bit* (*bi*nary dig*it*) and we shall use this word frequently. Thus we speak of 3 bits of information, a word length of 36 bits, a rate of 1000 bits per second, and so on.

A common mistake in trying to use the binary system in practical situations is to ignore the empty (blank) state. At first glance the games of tic-tac-toe (noughts and crosses), *go,* and Chinese checkers all appear to require one bit for every location on the board in order to describe the entire board position at any time—a 0 for you and a 1 for me in each location—but this ignores the need to indicate an empty location. Thus these games are more naturally represented in a ternary (base 3) system, and if we must use the binary system we can use two bits for each position.

The board positions of such games can be described in another way. By assigning labels (sequences of 0s and 1s) to the individual locations we could describe the entire board position by two lists, one of your locations and one of my locations. This illustrates the fact that the same situation can be described in many quite differently appearing ways, and the most suitable one depends on how we are going to process the information.

There are many other forms for representing information besides the binary notation. For example, this book uses (among other symbols) a set of 26 letters, both upper and lower case, 10 decimal digits, spaces of several sizes, a number of punctuation marks, and an occasional change in type font such as the use of *italics.* This system is in very widespread use and is in many respects well-suited to the human nervous system.

The Chinese system of writing uses thousands of distinct characters, but they are derived from fewer radicals which sometimes makes them a bit easier to understand. The Chinese system has some advantages over the alphabet but also has some serious disadvantages. Musical scores are another form for representing information, and the decimal number system is yet another.

Catalog numbers, part numbers of machines, and license plates often use combinations of letters and numbers to represent information. In most such applications the numbers are merely used as labels and have little or no real numerical use beyond this.

Rather than deal with each special system for representing information it is preferable to develop the theory of representing information in terms of a single, convenient system—and this turns out to be the binary one. The binary system is *not* useful for human use in the actual communication of information, but it does have simple theoretical properties that aid in developing an understanding of the theory. Furthermore, at the moment it is almost universal to use the binary system of representation inside large-scale digital computers, and, though it is possible that future technological discoveries could change this, it seems likely that computers will continue to use two-state devices for a long time to come.

The reduction, or if you wish, the transformation (encoding) from a given system of representation to a binary system is usually very easy to do, and thus the binary system provides a universal way station in going from any one particular representation to another form of representation. For example, consider using only the upper case system of letters as an information system. We need 26 states for the letters, another state for the space, and several states for punctuation, probably less than 64 states in all. We can therefore use 6 bits, since $2^6 = 64$, to represent all these states in any arbitrary way we wish. All we require is that distinct symbols in the original system go into distinct binary symbols. In particular we can use those shown in Table 2.1-2.

Table 2.1-2

A = 000 001	space = 000 000
B = 000 010	period = 100 101
C = 000 011	comma = 100 110
$\vdots$	$\vdots$
Y = 011 001	paragraph = 111 110
Z = 011 010	end of message = 111 111

Given a message in capital letters, we can now transcribe (encode) the message into binary symbols using the above table. Anyone who receives our message can, if he has the same table of equivalent symbols, decode the received message and recover the original one that was in capital letters.

AN EXAMPLE OF TEXTUAL ANALYSIS   2.2

Suppose we have a selection from a book that is already represented in the above 6-bit code for the letters, space, paragraph, and end of message symbols together with the miscellaneous punctuation marks that might be necessary. We wish to know the average number of letters in the words that the author used—perhaps for purposes of analyzing his style of writing. We could, of course, translate it back into alphabetic characters and read it directly. Another process that will achieve the same result is to look at the first group of 6 bits and ask if it is a space (000 000) or a paragraph symbol (111 110). In either case we tally 1 in the word count. If it is not one of these two we then ask if it is a punctuation mark, and if so we ignore it. If it is none of these, then automatically it is a letter (without doing any further inspection) and we tally 1 in the letter count. We then pick up the next 6 bits of the message and repeat the analysis, and so on, until the whole text is done, which is indicated by the end of message symbol (111 111). At the end of all the counting we have two sums, the number of words (since we are assuming that words begin with a space or a paragraph) and the number of letters. Dividing the second total by the first we have the average number of letters per word.

Figure 2-1 shows a flowchart of this process. While we shall study flowcharts in more detail in the next chapter, they are sufficiently familiar to most people so that they can follow Figure 2-1. We begin at START, set both totals to zero to remove any results left from earlier work, and then we READ NEXT SYMBOL. We then test for END OF MESSAGE. If it is, we go to the right. Otherwise we go down to the next diamond-shaped box and start to analyze the symbol. This diamond may send us to another diamond, but all the paths lead us back to READ NEXT SYMBOL except the one that goes to END.

If we simply follow the path imagining we are a machine and have the required text to read, then we see that we get the two totals WORD TOTAL and LETTER TOTAL, and at the END OF MESSAGE (symbol 111 111) we DIVIDE LETTER TOTAL BY WORD TOTAL to get the answer, and then END.

But let us be careful! What did we do with hyphenated words? Since we ignored punctuation marks we simply counted hyphenated words as a single word. Is that what is wanted? It depends on the purposes and beliefs of the person for whom the work is being done. Again, were there any double spaces? If so, we may be seriously inaccurate in our word count. We can, of course, make a small modification in our process to take care of these possibilities. If the text contained numbers such as 147, was that to be counted as one word, and if so is 1 478 two words? This vast sea of small questions and corresponding small modifications tends to be ignored in a first approach, but it is vital in the final analysis, as we shall see in Chapter 5, in dealing with a simple problem of geometry. It is what makes the blind, thoughtless use of a rigid, fixed computer routine so dangerous. At the same time the power to do the counting rapidly, cheaply, and accurately makes the computer extremely valuable on such tasks in actual practice.

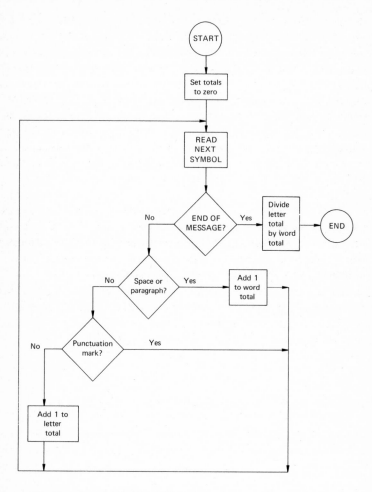

Figure 2-1 Flowchart for Section 2.3.

Evidently, the quality of the result does not depend on the particular machine which carries out the processes indicated in the flowchart, but rather on the general plan devised beforehand. (Unfortunately the actual details of the plan may depend on the machine we use.) In this example we have used an extremely simple *statistic*, average word length. In practice much more sophisticated statistics are used to settle questions of authorship and style[1] but the fundamental ideas are the same. Because of the importance of statistics in many applications of computers, we will develop some of the simpler ideas of statistics as we go along. Without any statistics we would not be able to understand many important applications of computers in modern society. With even a little statistics we can get an idea of how many of the complex things such as election predictions are possible, as well as some idea of what is actually involved in what you see on election night.

AN EXAMPLE OF A STATISTICAL TEST   2.3

Let us turn to an example of a computation that would use a bit more elaborate statistics.

Consider Table 2.3-1 in which we have listed the number of words of a given length that occur in randomly selected passages of 250 consecutive words from three books A, B, and C.

Table 2.3-1

word length	number of words in			remarks
	A	B	C	
1	6	5	7	too close
2	42	42	45	
3	44	54	33	two extreme values
4	17	33	24	
5	34	28	16	
6	21	27	16	too close
7	27	22	25	too close
8	11	11	23	
9	15	9	32	
10	18	4	5	
11	5	8	13	
12	4	2	5	
13	6	2	4	two extreme values
14	0	0	2	too small
15	0	1	0	
total	250	250	250	
score	1	2	5	

[1] L. Dolezel and R. W. Bailey, eds., *Statistics and Style*, American Elsevier, New York, 1969.

If I now tell you that two of the books are history books and one is a chemistry book, can you identify the chemistry book? How can we go about deciding which column is the "most different," since we expect the chemistry book to be different from the two history books? One plausible way is to circle the extreme of each line ("extreme" means farthest from the average of the line) as we have done. Notice that column C has five extreme values, A had one, and B had two, while many lines (1, 3, 6, 7, 13, 14, 15) have not been marked since "extreme" seems to be somewhat meaningless in these cases. Thus with some confidence (but not certainty) we predict that the numbers in column C, being the most different, came from the chemistry book—and in this case we are right.

But let us be clear about the matter. We have not *proved* that the numbers in column C are from the chemistry book, we have only made it plausible. And the plausibility rests both on our choice of using the extremes to measure the "difference in styles", and on the number of words used from each book. Larger samples would probably increase our confidence in our prediction. However, let us admit it, the test was merely plausible and in the final analysis somewhat arbitrary. But that is how we actually live our lives from moment to moment. We *assume* a great deal and act accordingly—we quickly estimate the chances. We will return to this topic in Chapter 12.

EXERCISES—2.3

1. Take three books, two of one style and one of another and tabulate word length counts for 200 consecutive words. Apply the above crude statistical test. Does it work? Do the styles seem to differ more than they are the same? How would you bet if you did not know which was which?

2. Design a different type of test to measure "differentness." Try it on the data of the text. Defend your reasons for preferring your test to the one used in the text.

THE GROWING IMPORTANCE OF INFORMATION   2.4

The computer is important in our society because it processes information rapidly, accurately, and economically. This implies that there is information to be processed. We need, therefore, to take a brief look at the growing importance of information to our society.[2]

[2] F. Machlup, *The Production and Distribution of Knowledge in the United States,* Princeton University Press, Princeton, 1962.

Each year that passes we spend increasingly more money and effort in creating, processing, transforming, storing, and finally retrieving information, and correspondingly we spend relatively less in the handling of the material aspects of our society such as agriculture and manufacturing.

The same is true in science. The classical picture of a scientist shows him dressed in a white coat in a laboratory doing something in the material world, perhaps pouring a chemical from one test tube into another, perhaps measuring some effect, or controlling some process by turning knobs. However, especially since the Second World War, which in many respects marks a sharp change in the way we do science, the truth is that scientists devote much of their time to examining and processing information and spend relatively little time in actual experimentation. In recognition of this change many recruiting ads and magazine illustrations now show people sitting around a conference table, or a man standing at a blackboard, rather than the traditional man in a white smock looking at a large collection of glassware.

De Solla Price has popularized the rate of growth of science in a couple of remarks:

1. The amount of knowledge in the typical field of science doubles every 10 to 15 years.
2. 80 to 90 percent of the scientists who ever lived are now alive.[3]

It takes only a little calculation to realize that at these rates scientific knowledge increases 100 to 1000 times each century, and furthermore, that most scientists are young.

Unfortunately for the classical picture, science has become so complex that it is often necessary to do a great deal of *data reduction* and *data transformation* to get from the raw measurements now possible to the desired conclusions. To take but a single example, the reduction of data from space shots[4] involves a tremendous amount of computation before the data can be understood by humans.

Even the design of an experiment is now apt to require a great

---

[3] *Science Since Babylon,* Yale University Press, New Haven, 1961.
[4] Total information requirements for the early Voyager program was said to be of the order of 10^8 to 10^{10} bits, while the rates for information transmission were 1000 bits per second. A rate of 10 million bits per second was suggested as a minimum requirement for the later shots.

deal of preliminary planning and computation *before* starting to build the equipment or starting the survey. Frequently, before the equipment is built or the survey is started some simulated measurements will be written down and then processed as if they were actual data to see if the data reduction process will reveal the kinds of effects that are being sought.

In many ways it is very fortunate that the large-scale digital computer came along when it did, otherwise many of the computing tasks we now seem to need would either be impossible or too expensive in manpower and time to make them worth doing. Probably the computer helped bring about the marked change in our attitude toward information processing that characterizes modern science, and no doubt the necessity for the large amounts of data processing has helped to develop computers. As is often the case, it is hard to know which is cause and which is effect. Much of the early development of computers in the United States was financed by the Federal government, indicating that the need (both civilian and military) was recognized and promptly acted upon.

It has been said that the main problem facing our society is learning to understand and cope with complexity, and this is very close to the truth in many areas. Computers are a powerful tool for coping rapidly with complex situations and as a result will play an increasingly prominent role in our society.

To a person who is outside the computing field a phrase like "data processing" is apt to suggest the simple transformations of numbers such as paycheck calculations, bills, and the relating of the position and direction coordinates of a space missile returning to earth in order to record properly some variable, say, the charged particle density in space. Data processing is indeed this kind of "number crunching," but it is also much more. The raw data may be very far removed from the conclusions, and millions of arithmetic operations may be necessary before the job is done. The machine processing of the Mars and Moon pictures are perhaps a better indication of the typical data processing job. In these trials of picture processing, changes in the contrast were tried, various smoothings were applied, sometimes using information from different shots to resolve difficulties, and many other changes were made in order to extract all we could from the little we had to go on.

An Aside on Information Theory

There is a body of knowledge known as *information theory* which brought together some scattered knowledge and added a lot more. It was developed by C. E. Shannon in 1948.[5] Much of its popularity lies in its attractive name which suggests that we have a theory for understanding what *information* is. The great success of the theory, however, probably rests on the fact that it never actually defines what information is. Instead, information theory *assumes* that a source of information exists and then examines questions that center around the rate at which this information can be transmitted (communicated) over suitable channels. Information theory is especially interested in the "noisy channels" through which the receiver gets the original message with some "noise" added on. In this case the receiver (machine or human) faces the problem of trying to deduce what the original message was before the noise was added. We shall follow the lead of information theory and not even try to say what information is. Rather we shall assume that there is some information at hand, and we will be concerned with how we can transform this information from one form of representation to another. We are transforming, not creating, information, but it may well be true that before the transformation we could not use the information and after the transformation we can use it, so in one sense we have created information.

THE BINARY NUMBER SYSTEM   2.5

We have already discussed the binary system for representing information; we now turn to the binary number system. This notation for representing numbers is used so often that it is necessary to discuss it in some detail.

The binary number system is formally like the decimal number system—indeed, it is often taught in school to illustrate how the decimal number system works. It is safe to say that if there is trouble in understanding the binary number system, then probably the fault lies in the failure to understand the decimal number system and not in the details of how to carry out various arithmetic operations.

[5]E. N. Gilbert, "Eighteen Years of Information Theory," *Science*, May 1966.

Decimal numbers use a positional notation in which the value of a decimal digit 0,1, ... ,9, depends on *where* it occurs in the number. Considering the decimal integers first, the number

$$7 \ 401 \equiv 7 \times 10^3 + 4 \times 10^2 + 0 \times 10^1 + 1.$$

The binary system is exactly the same except that the choice of digits is no longer 0,1, ... ,9, but is restricted to the two values 0 and 1, and we use powers of 2 rather than powers of 10. Thus the number in binary

$$101 \ 101 \equiv 1 \times 2^5 + 0 \times 2^4 + 1 \times 2^3 + 1 \times 2^2 + 0 \times 2^1 + 1$$
$$= 32 + 0 + 8 + 4 + 0 + 1 = 45 \text{ in decimal notation.}$$

From this we see that a string of 0 and 1 symbols *may* have a numerical value associated with it. In the above example the binary sequence 101 101 and the decimal sequence 45 have the same numerical value associated with them and are said to be the same number, or if you wish to be careful, they are *equivalent representations for the same number.* This leads to the equivalent representations shown below:

decimal	0	1	2	3	4	5	6	7
binary	0000	0001	0010	0011	0100	0101	0110	0111
	8	9	10	11	12	13	14	15
	1000	1001	1010	1011	1100	1101	1110	1111

It is true that a sequence of 0 and 1 symbols may have a numerical value associated with it, but it might be merely a part number of some machine encoded in binary notation and the digits have no real numerical significance. The same applies to social security numbers, phone numbers, and so on. Their numerical value has little or no useful meaning in general, though the phone number may give some information about the geographical location of the phone. Like beauty, the meaning assigned to a sequence of 0s and 1s lies in the eye of the beholder and not in the object itself. The treatment of fractional numbers lying between 0 and 1 is similar, but different in details not worth discussing here.

ERROR-DETECTING CODES   2.6

Since errors are all too common in recording, copying, and transmitting information, it is natural to examine what can be done besides trying to be careful, or doing something twice. A simple way to protect a message in binary form from isolated errors is to break the message up into equal length blocks and then add a single bit on the end of each block, choosing the value of the extra bit to be a 1 if there are an odd number of 1s in the block of message, and 0 if there are an even number of 1s. Thus in both cases there are an even number of 1s in the message block *plus* the check bit. If at any later time an odd number of 1s is found, then clearly at least 1 bit must be wrong, either in the original message block or in the check bit. This is called a *parity check bit.* When there are an odd number of 1s in the binary representation of a number it is said to have an *odd parity,* and for an even number an *even parity*.

In practice, when using this method of checking we need to use some common sense. If the blocks of the message are very long, then the possibility of the undetectable combinations of two, four, six, etc., errors is apt to be high, and obviously only blocks with an odd number of errors will be caught. Thus it is better to break a long message up into reasonably short blocks and apply a check bit to each block, the length being chosen to be short enough so that the probability of two or more errors is so small that it can be neglected in practice.

As an example of an error-detecting code we might encode the decimal digits into their natural binary form using 4 bits, and then add a 5th parity-check bit as in Table 2.6-1.

Table 2.6-1

		check bit			check bit
0	0000	0	5	0101	0
1	0001	1	6	0110	0
2	0010	1	7	0111	1
3	0011	0	8	1000	1
4	0100	1	9	1001	0

Thus we are representing the decimal digits as 5-bit symbols from which it is easy to recover (decode) the original value by dropping the last bit.

Similarly, in a computing machine which has *words* consisting of 36 bits, a single 37th bit is often added for checking purposes (done automatically inside the machine).

The extra parity bit is said to be "redundant" and measures part of the extra cost of catching isolated errors in the message.

EXERCISE–2.6
Encode the alphabetic example of Section 2.1 into a 7-bit error-detecting code.

AN INTERESTING EXAMPLE OF ERROR DETECTING   2.7

The problem of checking short messages that consist of letters, numbers, and possibly spaces (which is all that some simple keypunch machines can handle) is of common occurrence. Catalog names and numbers, license plate numbers, social security names and numbers, credit card identification, and phone numbers are all illustrations. Let us assign the following numerical equivalents:

space	goes into the value 0
A,B,C, ... ,Z	go into the values 1,2,3, ... ,26
0,1,2, ... ,9	go into the values 27,28, ... ,36

The binary number equivalents are shown in Section 2.5. (The difficulty of distinguishing the letter O from the digit 0 has led to the widespread use of Ø for the letter O.) To get an error-detecting system we propose that whenever we write out a sequence of these symbols we add on one more symbol which will be chosen so that the sum of all the symbols is exactly divisible by 37.

As an example, consider encoding the catalog number AQ2B9:

$$
\begin{array}{rl}
A & \rightarrow \quad 1 \\
Q & \rightarrow \quad 17 \\
2 & \rightarrow \quad 29 \\
B & \rightarrow \quad 2 \\
9 & \rightarrow \quad 36 \\
\hline
\text{total} & 85
\end{array}
$$

Dividing 85 by 37 we get the remainder of 11. If we want the remainder to be 0 (or 37) then this requires us to add $37 - 11 = 26$ so that the final sum, now $85 + 26 = 111 = 3 \times 37$, will be exactly divisible by 37. But 26 corresponds to the letter Z, so we make (define) the catalog number to be

AQ2B9Z.

If the total is exactly divisible by 37 then nothing (space) is added. Any time a machine reads an encoded catalog number a check computation can be made to see if an error has occurred (though a double error might occasionally escape detection), and if it has we can promptly stop processing the material and avoid compounding the error further. Thus, some common types of errors (or frauds in the case of credit card identification) can be found easily and promptly by the computing machine when the information is first entered into the system.

This code can be significantly improved when we recognize that one of the most common errors that humans make is the interchange of two symbols (usually adjacent ones) such as 39 becoming 93, or CF becoming FC. The above method does not detect this all-too-common type of mistake. The following modification of the encoding scheme will, however, discover this type of error. The modification consists of forming a *weighted sum* of the symbol values. An obvious way, though not the only one, is to weight the first symbol by 1, the second by 2, the third by 3, ... , the last (which is our redundant check symbol) by 6. We have therefore to compute

$$
\begin{array}{l}
1 \text{ times the value of A} = 1 \times \ \ 1 = \ \ \ \ 1 \\
2 \text{ times the value of Q} = 2 \times 17 = \ \ 34 \\
3 \text{ times the value of 2} \ = 3 \times 29 = \ \ 87 \\
4 \text{ times the value of B} = 4 \times \ \ 2 = \ \ \ \ 8 \\
5 \text{ times the value of 9} \ = 5 \times 36 = \underline{180} \\
\phantom{5 \text{ times the value of 9} \ = 5 \times 36}\text{total} \ \ = 310
\end{array}
$$

Dividing 310 by 37 gives the remainder of 14. We need to find an integer, call it x as in algebra, such that

$6x + 14$ is a multiple of 37.

The solution, which can always be found for any particular case we need, is in this case $x = 10$ which corresponds to the symbol J. Hence in this encoding method the result is

AQ2B9J

If the sum were divisible by 37 we would add a blank which in this method can be ignored.

Again it is clear that any single change in a character will be detectable because the sum will then no longer be exactly divisible by 37. But it is now also true that any interchange of characters, adjacent or not, will also change the sum by a number not divisible by 37 and hence will be detectable (unless they are the same letter, in which case it does not matter!). We leave it to the mathematically inclined to *prove* that no interchange can escape detection, which depends on the observation that 37 is a prime number.

We have, therefore, exhibited a simple encoding scheme which protects against isolated single errors as well as interchanges of two symbols by mistake. If this encoding is applied as early as possible, perhaps at the time the names (and addresses) are assigned, then the system gives a good deal of protection against the most common mistakes that humans are apt to make in dealing with such situations. Unless the method of encoding is known, and variants in the assigning of the weights may be used (one need not use the regular system of weights 1,2,3, ... , as we did), then the person who tries to make up, say, a credit card number, will about 36 out of 37 times make up one that will be immediately detected as a fraud by anyone who knows the encoding system.

Note that this system may be applied to variable length messages such as personal names. We merely add a single letter to the end of the man's name (while ignoring any periods he may have used after an initial). If we encode a message greater than 37 symbols in length we will find that we have to use the same weights more than once, and hence certain interchanges of letters which are physically remote will escape detection, but this is a small risk indeed.

There is, of course, the chance that the check symbol we add is blank. If so we do not bother to print it in a fixed length encoding system.

The purpose of these examples of encoding information is to show that there is a body of knowledge that can be applied to the representation of information so that in the transmission and recognition of encoded information any single error can be detected. (For more errors see the methods of the next section.)

EXERCISES—2.7

1. Encode BØQ27 as a simple error-detecting code, and as a weighted sum.

2. Encode A3B7C3 both ways.

3. Design a simple device for encoding in the weighted-sum code.

4. Discuss the practical details of a suitable variant of the weighted encoding system for variable length messages

ERROR-CORRECTING CODES (not an essential section) 2.8

The theory of error detection can be greatly extended. In particular, it has been extended to cover some *error correction,* meaning that at the receiving end an isolated error can not only be detected, but can also be corrected *from the information at hand at the receiving end.* Indeed, the theory has been extended to multiple error detection and correction up to any preassigned amounts.

We shall give only a simple example of an error correcting code. We merely sketch *how* it works and not *why* it works. For simplicity, assume that we are concerned only with the decimal digits encoded in their equivalent 4-digit binary form. We will assign the 4 binary digits to positions 3,5,6,7 of a 7-bit complete message symbol and we will compute the other three positions 1,2,4 of the message symbol using parity checks. We assign:

position 1 so that there is an even parity in positions 1,3,5,7

2 so that there is an even parity in positions 2,3,6,7

4 so that there is an even parity in positions 4,5,6,7

As an example, given the decimal digit 6, which in binary form is 0110, we write these digits in positions 3,5,6,7 as shown in the first line of Table 2.8-1.

Table 2.8-1

				position				
	1	2	3	4	5	6	7	
write the digit 6 in positions 3,5,6,7			0		1	1	0	
add check bit at position 1 using 1,3,5,7 for parity	1		0		1	1	0	
check bit at 2 using 2,3,6,7 for parity	1	1	0		1	1	0	
check bit at 4 using 4,5,6,7 for parity	1	1	0	0	1	1	0	= message
suppose that there is an error, say, in position 5	1	1	0	0	0	1	0	
					(error)			

When the 7-bit message is received we:

> Apply parity check 1 over 1,3,5,7
> It fails. Write 1 indicating a failure.
>
> Apply parity check 2 over 2,3,6,7
> It is satisfied. Write 0 on the left of the first digit we wrote indicating a success.
> We now have 01
>
> Apply parity check 4 over 4,5,6,7
> It fails. Write 1 on the left of the earlier digits.
> We now have 101

This number, 101, is the decimal 5 and indicates the position of the error—hence we change the fifth position we received, a 0, to a 1. This applies to any position, *including* the check positions 1,2,4.

EXERCISE—2.8
Apply the method and correction to the number 7 = 0111 where the error occurs in the third position; in the seventh position; in the first position.

SUMMARY   2.9

The purpose of this chapter has been to introduce the topic of the representation of information. Clearly, if we cannot represent information in a form that can be used by a computer then we cannot expect a computer to process it. While we have tried to separate two topics into two chapters, the representation of information and the representation of processes are actually intimately connected. In fact we did show one simple case of the representation of a process, that of finding the average length of words in a text.

We tried to make a careful distinction between the binary system of representation of information for situations in which all we require is separate labels (where we merely regard the sequence of 0s and 1s as a single symbol), and the binary number system in which we use the structure of the symbol to carry information (for example, the position of the 0 or 1 in the sequence of digits gives its corresponding value).

We have also tried to give some indication of the extent of the field of the representation of information by introducing the important topic of error control. This is a vast subject in its own right and can only be touched upon here. Indeed, these days the topic of error correcting can be (and has been) the subject of a two-day symposium.

We have discussed the representation of only decimal digits and alphabetical information. With a little thought the reader should realize that such things as musical scores can also be represented in a binary system. As a trivial (and inefficient) way we could assign a group of binary digits to represent the frequency (pitch) of the note, another group for the time duration, still other groups for each attribute we wish to consider. Many other examples are easily devised, such as scanning a picture as a television tube does.

But the reader should be careful; there are objects of common conversation like the classical trio of truth, beauty, and justice, for which we have no useful way of representing the idea. In a sense the letters themselves represent the ideas, but we cannot manipulate these representations to get anything useful from them. Until we can, we have no idea of how to use a computing maching to compute with such ideas. In view of their long history in philosophical debate it may be a very long time, if ever, before we can get any useful representation of such ideas and the relevant processes, and can thus apply machines to questions in these areas.

The topic of the representation of information is a very large and important one, one that is only gradually receiving the attention it needs in view of its fundamental role in computing and human communication. There have long been many scattered fragments—mathematicians have occasionally discussed the choice of symbols—but it is only just now coming into its own. Of necessity we have given only a glimpse of this large and important field.

CHAPTER 3

Jaipur Observatory, Jaipur, India (17th century)
From Magnum.

3

Representation of Processes

INTRODUCTION—MAKING FUDGE 3.1

Having examined the representation of information we now turn to the representation of processes. The natural languages, such as English, are perhaps better suited to describing *things* than they are for describing *processes.* Computing machines, however, process information, and in order to get them to do what we want, we must describe to the machine the processes we want done. The aim of this chapter is to further develop a notation, called *flowcharts*, that aids in describing some processes. We also develop slightly the method of using a somewhat stylized English to describe a process.

Cookbooks are devoted to describing the *processes* for cooking various foods. But, as any beginner in cooking soon discovers, cookbooks often leave out many simple but essential steps. In using a computing machine it is necessary to give *all* the details. Nothing can be left to the imagination since computing machines simply do not have imagination (though, as we shall see in Chapter 14, some limited aspects of imagination can be simulated).

As an example, consider Figure 3-1, a recipe from Betty Crocker's New Picture Cookbook (McGraw-Hill, New York, 1961).

Old-Fashioned Chocolate Fudge

2 cups sugar
2/3 cup milk
2 sq. unsweetened chocolate (2 oz.)
    or 1/3 cup cocoa
2 tbsp. light corn syrup
1/4 tsp. salt
2 tbsp. butter
1 tsp. vanilla
1/2 cup broken nuts

Combine sugar, milk, chocolate or cocoa, corn syrup and salt in saucepan. Stir over medium heat until chocolate melts and sugar dissolves. Cook to 234° or until a little dropped in cold water forms a soft ball. Stir occasionally. Remove from heat. Add butter. Cool to lukewarm without stirring. Add vanilla. Beat until thick and no longer glossy. Quickly stir in nuts. Pour into buttered 8 or 9" square pan. When set, cut into squares. Makes 36 (1-1/2") pieces.

Figure 3-1

On the upper part of the page, above the recipe shown here, are eight general remarks about how to make candy and a set of tests for recognizing various balls of fudge and their equivalent temperature. Furthermore, in the front of the book are several short sections on *kitchen know-how* and *how to do it.*

We can easily convert this verbal description into a picture, called a flowchart (Figure 3-2). A flowchart contains no new information; it merely presents the information in a different form. Several times the flowchart shows a *loop* where a loop is implied in the word description (still other loops could be indicated). For example, testing the ball of fudge may be done quite a few times before the goal is reached. The flowchart does not tell how long between tests, something that you would have to think seriously about if you were building a robot to do the job. Indeed, if you were trying to build a machine to make fudge according to this recipe you would soon find that there were a lot of small details that had been left out. Some of them are partially answered by the remarks at the head of the page, which may be considered as subprocesses (we shall call them *subroutines*), while other details are partially covered by the remarks in the front of the book.

In many respects a computing machine may be viewed as a giant, flexible robot with no knowledge except that which you give it in specific detail. This is why it is necessary to give the machine an enormous amount of detail when a problem of even moderate complexity is to be done.

Note that in the flowchart we used variously shaped boxes for various types of information. In particular we used diamond shapes for decisions, and we labeled the exits from the box according to the possible outcomes. This notation is the same as we used in the previous chapter.

In so simple and familiar a process as fudge making a flowchart does not add much, if anything, to clarity. But, in more complicated processes, understanding *the flow of the control*—which is what we are really doing—is often essential if the whole process is to be understood. Furthermore, the flowchart approach tends to force one to think of *all* the necessary details and thus serves as an aid in organizing one's thinking. When we have a complete flowchart, we have a complete set of instructions (at that level of discussion).

EXERCISE—3.1
Draw a flowchart for your favorite recipe. Have you left out any essential details?

LEVELS OF FLOWCHARTING   3.2

In one sense the flowchart was completely detailed, but if we try to describe just which muscles to move at what times in the process of making the fudge, then the above diagram is completely superficial since it shows only the overall organization without the fine details.

It is necessary, therefore, when planning to draw a flowchart, to decide on the level of detail to be shown. There is no such thing as a completely detailed flowchart. There are only those that are complete at some agreed-upon level of description. In a complex process—perhaps the process to be used at a missile base to recognize an enemy target, assign equipment, and then guide the missile to the hoped-for interception—it is common practice to first draw large blocks (large in the sense that they imply much detail will lie inside and not in the sense that they are physically large), and then later expand the separate boxes into more detail. That is, each original box becomes several smaller interrelated boxes. Later still, each of these boxes will be expanded further.

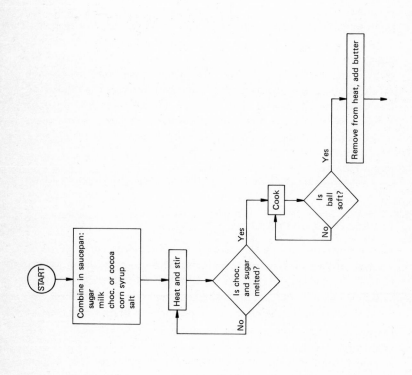

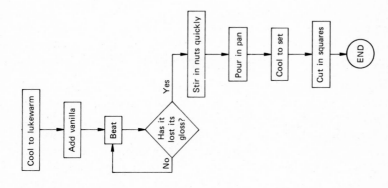

Figure 3-2

At each stage there is an implied level of detail, as well as the idea that by continuing the expansion process we will produce still further details. There is a final level of drawing, of course, and at that level it is *assumed* that people who are reasonably educated in the field will understand *with no ambiguity* exactly what is meant. But if a nonexpert tries to read the final detailed diagrams he generally finds that there are still many places where he does not know exactly what is meant.

AN EXAMPLE: FREQUENCY DISTRIBUTIONS   3.3

As a first example of describing a process, suppose we have the lengths of, say, a few hundred twigs measured to the nearest inch, and we wish to know the number of twigs there are of each length. Suppose further that the lengths run from 1 inch to not more than 25 inches. We are being asked to make a frequency distribution, just as we did for word lengths in the example in Chapter 2.

This time we propose to analyze more carefully the process of making the frequency distribution on a computer. We are assuming that the lengths of the twigs are already represented in a form that can be read by the machine. We begin by choosing 25 locations in the storage unit of the machine where we will store the answers to the question "How many twigs of the given length are there?" These locations must be given names so that we can refer to them.

In the earliest use of machines, a location in the machine storage unit was referred to by a number, say location (or address) 1732 (but usually in binary notation instead of decimal). This immediately produced a needless confusion between "the name of the location" and "the number stored at that location." Furthermore, the numerical naming of addresses is difficult for humans to use. As a result of these troubles it is now conventional to use location names that begin with a letter of the alphabet, though numerical digits and other symbols such as parentheses may occur in the middle of the name, if we wish. At this level of the flowchart we will pass over how the machine goes from the names we give the addresses to the binary numbers the machine actually uses as the addresses, only observing that this is a simple table look-up, something that a machine can do and which is therefore best left to the machine (see Section 3.7).

For mnemonic reasons we shall use in our problem of counting twig lengths the names

$$L(1), L(2), L(3), \ldots, L(25)$$

for the names of the (imagined) 25 lines on a sheet of paper corresponding to ones we would use if we had to do it by hand. These, for the moment, are merely symbols that we are using for addresses of the locations in the machine's storage unit. Next, we need to recall that the machine is *not* like a blank page. Frequently it still has written in it whatever the last problem left, so it is necessary to set initially the number at each location to 0 (this vital step is all too often overlooked by the beginner).

We next READ the first length as a number from, say, a standard Hollerith punched card. At this point we perform a logically crucial step and regard this number not as a length but as part of the name of a location by inserting it into L( ). As an illustration, for the length seven inches, we construct L(7), meaning "the name of the number stored on line 7." We now have the name L(7) of the line (location) where we wish to tally a one count, so we add 1 to the sum (tally) on that line and store the new sum on the same line, thus replacing the old sum. This ambiguity in the meaning associated with a number—first it was thought of as a length in inches and then it was thought of as a line number on an imagined sheet of paper—is one of the fundamental reasons why a digital computer can be so powerful. As we indicated in Chapter 2, the meaning of a number does not reside in the sequence of digits used to represent it but rather in how we process the digits.

The instruction we use to do the adding of 1 to the tally is

$$L(X) = L(X) + 1$$

meaning "the new number of line X is the old number on line X plus 1," thus erasing (or displacing) the old value.

Note that this is a violation of the usual mathematical convention. Whereas mathematical notation is usually static (that is, the meaning or value of a symbol does not change during a single problem), in computing it is usual to regard the notation as being dynamic (that is, the same symbol can have a changing meaning as the problem

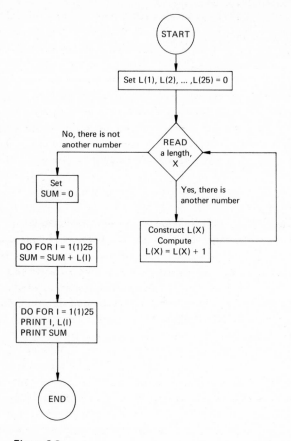

Figure 3-3

evolves). Perhaps a more flagrant-appearing violation of the same type is the equation

N = N + 1

which is logically equivalent to the preceding instruction. In computing circles the objections from the mathematical and logical purists about this new use of the equality sign (=) are generally ignored, and the old symbol for "equality" is appropriated to designate "is replaced by," or "takes the new value which is given on the right." Sometimes an arrow (←) is used instead of the equality sign, but it is pure pedantry to insist on using arrows.

Having read and processed one number we "loop back" and read another number and process it in the same way, and so on, until there are no more numbers to be read. Thus we are using the READ as a decision box: "Yes, there is another number" means process it and try again, while "No, there is not another number" means break out of the loop. On some machines it might be necessary to put in a trailing card with, say, a negative number and use a test on the sign of the number to recognize the end of the data. The details of just what method we use depend on the machine and are of no great interest here.

If we want to know the total number of twigs counted we can compute the total of all the sums on each line and put this total at a location called SUM. It might look as if we would need 24 additional instructions to get this sum. However, most higher level languages have instructions in a stylized English which permit the compression of the instructions into a small loop that is repeated the proper number of times. Thus a program resembling

```
SET SUM  = 0          (Initialize to zero to remove what
                       might be left in the location)
DO FOR I = 1(1)25     (Do the following steps starting with
                       I = 1 and going by steps of 1 until
                       I = 25)
    SUM = SUM + L(I)
```

Note both that we have again used a dynamic notation, and that the DO FOR instruction is really a loop in disguise. We could have replaced the first loop by a DO FOR if we had wished, but in the form we wrote the loop it automatically accommodates an indefinite number of twigs. The DO FOR loop we just drew (Figure 3-4) is fixed to handle exactly 25 different lengths.

The easiest way to convince yourself that you know what is going on is to act like a machine and try to follow the diagram. Suppose for trial purposes we assume we have five twigs of lengths 3, 2, 4, 2, 2. Then we proceed as follows:

START

SET[1] L(1) = L(2) = ... = L(25) = 0

READ a length, 3

Construct address L(3)

Take the 0 from address L(3), add 1, and store the SUM,
    now = 1, in L(3)

Go back to READ a length, 2

Construct address L(2)

Take the 0 from address L(2), add 1, and store the sum, now = 1,
    in L(2)

Go back to READ a length, 4

Construct address L(4)

Take the 0 from address L(4), add 1, and store the sum, now = 1,
    in L(4)

Go back to READ a length, 2

Construct address L(2)

Take the 1 from L(2), add 1, and store the sum, now = 2, in L(2)

Go back to READ a length, 2

Construct address L(2)

Take the 2 from address L(2), add 1, and store the sum, now = 3,
    in L(2)

Go back to READ (nothing)

Hence go out the No branch and set the location called SUM
    equal to 0

Take SUM, now = 0, add the number in L(1) which is 0, and store
    as SUM, now = 0

Take SUM, now = 0, add the number in L(2) which is 3, and store
    as SUM, now = 3

Take SUM, now = 3, add the number in L(3) which is 1, and store
    as SUM, now = 4

Take SUM, now = 4, add the number in L(4) which is 1, and store
    as SUM, now = 5

Since we have taken lengths only as large as 4 the further steps in
computing SUM will each add a zero and leave SUM unchanged; hence
we omit them here. Thus we have finally:

---

[1] We could use DO FOR I = 1(1)25
                    L(I) = 0 if we wished.

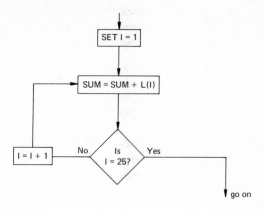

Figure 3-4

L(1) = 0
L(2) = 3
L(3) = 1
L(4) = 1

⋮

SUM = 5

as we should, SUM meaning "the number of twigs" and *not* "the sum of the lengths of the twigs."

Suppose next that we had wanted to know the average length of the twigs. A little thought shows that if on line 2 in the original example, that is, in L(2), we have found the number 3, this means that there are three twigs of length 2 inches, so their total length is 3×2 inches = 6 inches. By similar reasoning we can see that in our problem when we want the total length of all the twigs which we refer to as SUM2 (SUM2 is just a convenient name for another location) the length is found by computing

$$SUM2 = (0 \times 1) + (3 \times 2) + (1 \times 3) + (1 \times 4) + (0 \times 5)$$
$$= 6 + 3 + 4 = 13$$

Finally,

$$AVERAGE = SUM2/SUM = 13/5 = 2.6 \text{ inches}$$

Is this the correct answer? If so, we have some, though not complete, confidence that our instructions to the machine for the original problem are correct.

In more definite detail, in the general case if we multiply "the line number" by the "sum of that line," namely L( ) which is the name we use for the number of twigs of length ( ), we get the contribution to SUM2 from all the twigs of that length. Thus if we add all the products of line number (twig length) times the number on the line, namely L( ), we get the total length of all the twigs SUM2. Dividing by the number of twigs, SUM, we get the average length. This process we can incorporate in the DO FOR loop by adding an instruction

$$SUM2 = SUM2 + I \times L(I)$$

where, of course, L(I) is the number on line I. Remember to set SUM2 = 0 before starting (do it outside the loop!). What we do is clear, the details are not of great importance. It is now evident that the average twig length is easily obtained from the frequency distribution.

EXERCISE—3.3
Draw a flowchart to get the average twig length from the L(I) and SUM.

OTHER FREQUENCY DISTRIBUTIONS   3.4

Suppose that the twigs had been measured to the nearest half inch rather than to the inch. We would need 50 lines for the ½", 1" 1½", ... 25". To get the line numbers we could simply multiply the length by 2 and then go on as before. Of course a correction would have to be made at the end for the factor of 2 in calculating the average length, but the details are easy to figure out.

Suppose next we had a collection of fruits, say oranges, apples, bananas, etc. How are we to get from the name to the proper line so we can add 1 to its sum? One way would be to simply compare the word "orange" when it occurred with the line names until a match occurred (which is what you would do if you were doing it by hand) and having found the matching line you would add 1 to the sum on that line. Alternatively, one could imagine a preliminary encoding of the names *orange, apple, banana,* etc., to 1, 2, 3, etc., at the time the data is first read in. We could then proceed as before, provided we remember to uncode at the end so that the poor human reading the results has it in a form suitable for him rather than (as is too often the case) left in the form convenient for the machine.

This illustrates a typical situation: the form of the representation of the information (the name *orange, apple,* etc.) affects the processing of the information. The use of the letters ORANGE or the encoded 1 makes a difference: one form is better suited for humans, the other for machines. The task of encoding can best be done by the machine rather than the human.

In the above simple example, both processes, encoding first or searching for a match, require about the same amount of machine effort. But if there were a great deal of processing of the same data, the encoding would pay off handsomely. To encode we simply make a table of equivalent names and search in it to get from the name ORANGE to the number 1, while when we are going back during the decoding for the output we know what line in the table to read to get the name and do not need to search. The computation of the average would, of course, be nonsense in this example.

EXERCISE—3.4
Supply the corrections if the twigs are measured in ½" steps; in ¼" steps.

A SERIAL BINARY ADDER   3.5

Digital computers may be divided into two types, *serial* and *parallel,* depending on their internal engineering details. In the parallel machine all the digits of a binary number are sent at the same time (in parallel) along a set of wires, while in a serial machine the digits are sent one at a time (serially) down the same wire, usually with the least significant digit first. The digits appear in carefully controlled *time slots.* For the number 296, first the 6 would be sent, then the 9, and finally the 2.

As another example of describing a process (this time relevant to the machine design itself), consider how a pair of binary numbers can be added when the digits are presented serially, the least significant digit first. First, let us consider a simple special case which we hope will be typical and from which we can easily see the general case. Suppose we want to add 00111101 to 01010110. Thus

$$
\begin{array}{l}
\left.\begin{array}{l} 00111101 \\ 01010110 \end{array}\right\} \text{\textit{the two numbers to}} \\
 \text{\textit{be added}} \\
\text{\textit{carry digits}} \rightarrow \underline{1111100} \\
 10010011 \leftarrow \text{\textit{sum}}
\end{array}
$$

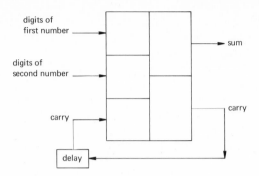

Figure 3-5 Adder.

where the third line shows the *carry digits* from the previous column. We start, as in decimal addition, at the extreme right column, $1 + 0 = 1$ and a zero carry in the next column to the left. The next column is $0 + 1 = 1$ and a zero carry. The third column is $1 + 1 = 0$ plus a carry that is written in the next (to the left) column. In the fourth column we have $1 + 0 + 1 = 0$ plus a carry. In the next column we have $1 + 1 + 1 = 1$ plus a carry, and so on.

So much for the special case. In the general case of adding any two binary numbers we see that each time (after the first) there are 3 digits to be added, 1 from each of the two numbers and 1 from the carry from the previous position (which may of course be a 0). Thus we have three streams of digits on the left of our diagram (Figure 3-5). The output on the right of the diagram is two streams, the first being the sum of the two numbers, and the other being the carry digit that will be fed back after a suitable delay (one time interval) into the left side.

The rules for forming the digits of the stream of the sum are:

   0 if there are zero or two 1s in the input
   1 if there are one or three 1s in the input

The rules for forming the carry digit are:

   0 if there are zero or one 1s in the input
   1 if there are two or three 1s in the input

Notice that we must be sure that there is no carry entering the first time we add (from some earlier addition perhaps). Also note that it is possible that the output sum is 1 bit longer than the longest of the input numbers.

In this example we get a glimpse of how a computing machine might work. We have drawn the flowchart of a binary adder down to a certain level of detail. Further expansion of the diagram might ask how we determine the number of 1s there are in the three inputs so that we can determine the two outputs. At a still further level of engineering we would have to give the detailed connection of components.

EXERCISE—3.5

Using two *half adders,* each of which merely adds two streams to produce the corresponding outputs for the sum and carry, show how a single complete adder can be built. Note that both of the half adders cannot have a carry at the same time.

A SKETCH OF A SERIAL BINARY MULTIPLIER 3.6

As a further example of flowcharts, consider the design of a *serial binary multiplier.* Again we start with a special case to get ourselves oriented. The following shows how two particular binary numbers are multiplied.

$$
\begin{array}{r}
1101 \\
\underline{1011} \\
1101 \\
1101 \\
0000 \\
\underline{1101} \\
\hline
10001111
\end{array}
$$

(Copy the multiplier if the multiplicand has a 1 and copy 0s if it has a zero, shift each copy one to the left of the preceding, and finally add all the partial products.) It would be rather complex to construct all this from scratch. Therefore we resort to adding each line of the product to the current partial sum of products, making use of the adder of the last section. In the upper loop of Figure 3-6 we imagine the multiplicand as circulating around a loop so that the digits are presented one at a time and with n (where there are at most n digits to the numbers) zeros in front of the n digits of the multiplicand. However, note that we send

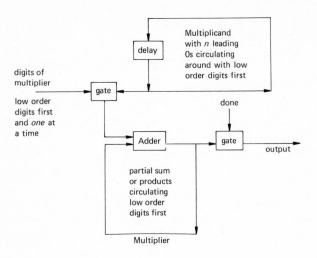

Figure 3-6

each number with the low order digits first, so that the n leading zeros come last in time. We also imagine a unit delay that we have specifically indicated.

The partial sum of products is also circulating in the lower loop but without a delay. The effect of the delay in the upper loop is to shift the digits one to the left each cycle as they should be. The first time around the multiplicand is added, if the multiplier digit is 1, to the initial zeros of the partial sum. The second time around, if the multiplier has a 1, the multiplicand is added to the first partial product, but due to the delay, it is added one position to the left, as it should be. Following the diagram step by step, each time around the multiplicand is added if the corresponding multiplier is a 1 and is not added if it is a 0, and each time the effect of the delay is to shift the digits one further to the left. When all is done, the lower gate opens and the product (double length and lowest order digit first) is sent out.

Here we see how block diagrams are built up out of smaller blocks, rather than as we have in the past from the larger blocks to the smaller blocks. There is no rigid rule, but from the point of view of this book we shall usually go from the larger to the smaller rather than build up from the smaller to the larger blocks. In practice both approaches are often used more or less at the same time to assure ourselves that what we now contemplate can indeed be done later when it comes to that level of expansion.

HASH TABLES 3.7

In the previous chapter we examined error-detecting and error-correcting codes both for their own interest, and to indicate some of the vast amount of material that is already known. In this section we examine the problem of table lookup for the same two reasons. Table lookup can be very expensive in machine time if there are many items to be searched to find a match.

Consider, for example, the lookup problem of a hotelkeeper. He can easily construct a table to answer, "Given the room number, what is the name of the temporary occupant?" But usually he is asked the reverse, "Given the name of the temporary occupant, what is his room number?" To answer this by searching rooms until he found a match he would have to examine, on the average, about half the rooms in his hotel before finding a given name.

Because this general kind of problem of table lookup occurs so often (we had it in the coding and decoding of fruit names), methods have been developed to cope with it. Resuming the hotel example, suppose the hotelkeeper has 1000 rooms in the hotel and it is often close to fully occupied. How can he use a computer economically to help him?

The ideas of a *hash table* and a *hash total*[2] are the basic keys. Our method is to derive from the name of the person a number which we call the hash total, which has no real meaning but is more convenient to use than is the original name. While there are many ways of getting a hash total, we shall use one particularly simple trick. With about 1000 names on the list, we arbitrarily make a hash table of 2048 possible entries (11 binary digits). From the name of the person, which we assume is punched in alphabetic characters but appears in the machine as a sequence of 0s and 1s, we take the first 11 bits as if they were a binary number, add to this the next 11 bits, add to this the next 11 bits, and so on, until we have exhausted all the digits (we may have to supply extra zeros at the end to complete a line). This sum is called the

---

[2]The name has a long history of evolution and once had a very different meaning.

hash total and it gives us a number that is uniquely derived from the name. A particular name always leads to the same hash total. Of course, the same hash total could come from completely different names, and this leads to difficulties that we will cope with shortly.

When someone first registers we write his name and compute its hash total. We then enter the table at the place given by the hash total just computed. If we find all zeros (a blank) opposite this address, then we know it is not in use and we write the original name *plus* his room number. But suppose, by chance, some other registered guest has already used the same hash total. When we enter the table we find a name, not all zeros, and we then search downward in the 2048 locations in the table for the first empty line and put the new guest's name and room number there. Since there are about twice as many lines available as there are guests we will generally find a blank line very soon.

When we get a query and try to use this table, we first compute the hash total from the supposed guest's name, and then we go to that place in the table. If we find the name we started with there, then we have what we want because the room number follows. But if the name does not match, then we search down to find a name match—and again we have the desired room number. If we find a blank then there is no such name registered.

The deletion of a name when a guest leaves is not straightforward, since it is necessary to examine the immediately following entries to see if they have the same hash total, and if they do we must move them up to close any gaps that might appear.

The hash total method is a simple device to avoid most of the searching. By controlling the ratio of the number of rooms, 1000, to the number of places where we search, 2048, we control the ratio of the average search time to wasted storage space in the machine. The function of the hash total is to get a convenient address from the name and to break up some of the structure that normally occurs in names and which tends to bunch them in parts of the storage and leave large gaps elsewhere in the table.

EXERCISES—3.7

1. Devise another trick for making a hash total.

2. Write an essay on the hash table method.

3. Draw a flowchart for finding the room number from the name.

THE FLOWCHART FOR THE FREQUENCY OF
WORD LENGTHS 3.8

In Chapter 2 we showed a frequency table of word lengths for three books (Table 2.3-1). In a major study of writing style, for example, such a step would appear as a single box in a flowchart. When it came time to carry out the flowchart the particular box would have to be expanded to a more detailed flowchart showing, much as we did before, how to get the frequency distribution given the word length. Still later in the process the part using the word length would have to be expanded into detailed instructions showing how to find the word length and how to recognize a word. We suggested the far too trivial rule of "space and paragraph to start words and ignore all punctuation marks" to delimit a word, and the simple act of counting the letters one by one to find the word length. In practice it would be much more complicated.

This is a basic pattern for doing large problems. First a flowchart using large blocks is drawn. At some later time the individual blocks are expanded. At a still later time they are further expanded. And so it proceeds until finally everything is spelled out in terms of some specific language, either the machine language or some other language for which a translator exists to get it into the machine language. We do not wish to get enmeshed in the details because they are not important to us at this moment. It is important to realize, however, that at every stage of expansion there will be new questions, and sometimes surprises, to be answered before the expansion can be completed. We will be satisfied here if the point is made that it *must* be possible to expand each and every statement, or remark, into specific, exact instructions in some given language. There can be no waving of hands and saying "Any fool knows!" There must be definite, precise instructions.

EXERCISE—3.8
Draw a flowchart for making word frequency counts.

PHILOSOPHY 3.9

It is in the nature of complex situations that one first forms the larger picture and expects later to be able to fill in the details when that step becomes necessary—meaning, sometimes, many man-years of work later—but at the time that the crude flowchart is made, the details are simply not known.

At conception one cannot possibly see all the details, and it is an act of faith that when the time comes the individuals who are to carry out the expansion will be able to expand the boxes in the flowchart properly. Of course at the early stages the more suspicious boxes will be examined with more care than others, but surprises await anyone doing something new or novel. It is in the nature of research and progress that occasionally everything is not foreseen, and when the time comes the diagram or plan simply cannot be expanded properly. This accounts for some of the failures on large projects.

As we said before, perhaps the central problem of our society is complexity—certainly it is of increasing importance—and about the only tool we have for coping with complexity is to try to break the complex situation into interrelated smaller pieces, and in time these pieces into still smaller pieces, and so on. Unfortunately, as will be shown by an example in Chapter 5, the attempt to abandon the overall view, after the first breakdown into smaller units, can lead to a loss of efficiency if not to a greater disaster. Yet what else is there to do?

About the only answer to this dilemma is what I shall call "philosophy." This word implies not the almost sterile philosophy of the professional philosophers, but rather the gradual acquisition of somewhat vague broad principles and a feeling for how things will go before a detailed look is made. All too often, in the author's opinion, once the broad breakdown into smaller pieces is made, it is then assumed that the details can be safely left to technicians. Sometimes this works, but frequently it results in failure. An overall view must somehow be kept throughout all the later stages, and there must be a willingness to restart when some unforeseen things come up rather than trying to smother them with a hasty "patch."

SUMMARY   3.10

We have shown that a flowchart, box diagram, or something like them,[3] is almost a necessary tool for coping with complexity. It is not an ideal tool, but we seem to have nothing else to use when we are faced with

---

[3]Another tool, similar to the flowchart, is the *decision table*, which is much used in business applications. In the decision table the logical decision structure is prominently displayed and the processes are minimized. For many purposes the

real complexity. And let me repeat, in many respects complexity is the central problem of our society, whether in science, engineering, business, government, city planning, transportation, social structure, or what have you, and the flowchart is often a very useful tool in attacking these complex situations. Stylized English is another powerful tool for describing processes. Note, however, that modifications to flowcharts and box diagrams are usually far more easily and safely made than are modifications to sentence-like programs.

We begin with a problem that is reasonably well described, and try to find some process that can be used to solve it. In simple problems these steps follow one another, but in complex, ill-defined situations there is apt to be some interaction between what we want to do (the problem) and the process of doing it (the solution). What we can do often shapes what we want to do.

We are *supposing* that the solution (process) we find can be represented in the form of a flowchart (though we have noted that other forms of solution can be used when convenient). In a very real sense the flowchart is the solution to the problem.

In trying to fill out the details of the flowchart we are sometimes led to modifications of the solution, and sometimes even of the problem itself: We proceed step by step, elaborating the early crude diagrams to more detailed diagrams, each stage requiring a corresponding level of detail. At the last stage of expansion of the flowchart the details that are necessary to supply to a machine must be specific at every point. There can be no vague appeal to common sense that the machine simply does not have.

The flowchart is an important tool because the actual programming of the machine proceeds from it. Once the flowchart is completed the rest is mechanical detail that programmers can carry out, but a knowledge of how this is done is essential if the planning is to be reasonable. Too often people who do not know how to program in detail make grandiose flowcharts that are difficult to get onto a machine without a great waste of machine time and extra coding effort. Thus, each stage must have one eye on the following stages, the other eye on the earlier stages—a difficult but necessary feat.

---

decision table approach is preferable to the flowchart approach. However, decision tables will not be discussed further in this book because they are a bit more technical than flowcharts.

CHAPTER 4

Napier's Bones (Baron von Napier, 1550-1617)
From the original in the IBM Corporation Antique Calculator Collection.

4

The Digital Computer

Having examined the representation of information and the representation of processes, we now examine the processor of information, the digital computer.

Rather than merely give a description of how current computers are built, we shall discuss a little of *why* they are the way they are. In this manner we can give some feeling for the structure of a computer independent of the current engineering details of *how* computers are built.

STORAGE 4.1

It is evident that if machines are to take advantage of their great speeds, they cannot wait at every turn for the relatively slow human to supply the next piece of information or the next step in the process. Instead, all the information and a complete description of the whole process must be available to the machine at speeds that are comparable with its basic speed of operation. Some large problems do read in new information and/or further processes as the problem goes on, but even then large blocks are usually entered at one time.

This observation implies that the machine must have the ability to store and retrieve information from a large, high-speed storage device. For some years now (1970) this large, high-speed storage device has generally been built out of very small magnetic doughnut-shaped cores with wires threaded through them. The cores can be magnetized in one of two directions by passing suitable currents through the wires. Thus a single core can store 1 bit of information as well as read it out when necessary. Gradually, thin magnetic films and plated wires have been coming into use to serve the same purpose. Many other technologies, especially optical ones, have been proposed, and some have been tried out in practice. Up till now, however, only magnetic storage is well established.

To form the main storage the cores are arranged in a regular array. The most recent standard is to assign 8 bits to 1 *byte*, and assign anywhere from 2 to 9 bytes to a *word*. The words are numbered (named) by their *addresses* (locations), running from 000 ... to the highest address, often $32,767 = 2^{16} - 1$. Adjacent addresses do not mean that the cores are physically adjacent, but the physical layout does not affect the user. Each time he uses the same address he gets the same set of cores.

As a general rule, the reading in of new information destroys whatever information was stored in that location: the new information replaces the old information that was there. It is rather like a system of house numbers. The address gives the location in storage where the information is stored. The address also serves as the name of the information when it is stored inside the machine, and each new occupant displaces the previous one at that address.

The high-speed read-in and read-out storage is usually so expensive that backup storage devices are supplied that are cheaper per bit but slower, or possibly are "read only" (meaning that either they are not capable of having something new entered or else are very slow in reading in new information).

In the early days of computing much emphasis was put on the fact that numbers and instructions were stored in the same kind of storage unit, and since both were sequences of 0s and 1s, we could treat the two different kinds of objects in the same manner if we pleased. We now realize that there are differences, not in representation to be sure, but in the way we want to treat the two different kinds of things, and accordingly we process them somewhat differently. However, we may use parts of the numbers as instructions—as we did in making L( ). The old idea of complete interchangeability, while charming and appealing, got us into unnecessary confusions and troubles, and it is not emphasized nearly so much these days. However, now and then one still does see it.

THE ARITHMETIC UNIT 4.2

Because of the widespread use of arithmetic in so many different processes most computers have an *arithmetic unit* that is capable of doing addition, subtraction, multiplication, and division on binary numbers. In principle there need be no such arithmetic unit, and more primitive, less efficient methods could be used to do the arithmetic. Except in very special situations, though, this is not done in commercially available machines.

The main part of the arithmetic unit, from the user's point of view, is the *accumulator*, where sums (and differences) of numbers are accumulated. In a few very big machines there are several accumulators, but logically this is not important. Numbers go into the accumulator from storage and can be read out from the accumulator back into storage.

We have already (Chapter 3) glanced at how a serial adder and a corresponding multiplier unit might be built, so we need not say much more about how the arithmetic unit works (except to note that in practice there are engineering details that are different from those we presented whose net effect is to speed up the processes significantly). The place where the multiplier number is stored is often called the MQ register.

Because in practice we want to transform and combine digits in other ways than by the four arithmetical operations, the arithmetic unit has many other features besides the ability to add, subtract, multiply, and divide two numbers. Among other operations it can also perform what is called *logical addition*.

In each position the binary digits are combined as they would be in normal addition,

$$0 \oplus 0 = 0$$
$$0 \oplus 1 = 1$$
$$1 \oplus 0 = 1$$
$$1 \oplus 1 = 0$$

except that the carry to the next position is omitted. This is also often called *exclusive or*.

Another logical operation is ∅R, often denoted by +. In this operation a 1 is placed in each position where there is 1 in either, *or* both, of the two input numbers.

$$0 + 0 = 0$$
$$0 + 1 = 1$$
$$1 + 0 = 1$$
$$1 + 1 = 1$$

Finally there is the logical AND, (·), which puts a 1 in each position where there is a 1 in the first *and* in the second numbers in the same position

$$0 \cdot 0 = 0$$
$$0 \cdot 1 = 0$$
$$1 \cdot 0 = 0$$
$$1 \cdot 1 = 1$$

It is the logical instructions (discussed in more detail in Chapter 12) that permit the machine to handle complex logical situations—and in the common folklore are what make the machine a "threat to humans."

There are *shift operations* that, as the name implies, shift the bits left or right as far as is indicated by the instruction. Thus a bit in one position in a word can be combined with a bit in some other position in another (or the same) word.

THE CONTROL UNIT   4.3

The whole computing machine is driven by a *control unit*. What it controls is the flow and processing of the information. This unit gets its directions on what to do from the instructions of the computer program the human supplies (in some form). Among other things, the control unit needs to know where in storage to find the next instruction of the process being worked on. The address of this next instruction is stored in a fixed place in the machine that we shall call the *current address register*. Typically, though not always, the computing machine is designed to take the instructions from successive locations in storage, and therefore the number in the current address register is automatically increased by 1 every time it is used by the control unit.

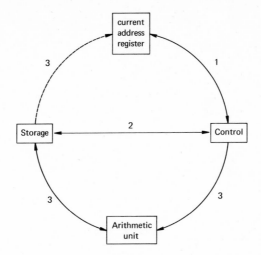

Figure 4-1 The basic three-step cycle of the computer.

For example, after following the instruction located in 1728, the next instruction would be in 1729, the next in 1730, etc. The exceptions will be discussed in Section 4.4.

Since the control unit is the heart of the machine we shall examine the three steps in the basic cycle of operations—the heartbeat of the computer.

The cycle begins with the control unit getting the address that is stored in the current address register. The next step is to use this address to fetch from storage the instruction to be done. In the typical one-address machine, this instruction consists of two parts:

1. the actual instruction to do something (like ADD or SUBTRACT)
2. an address giving the location of the information that is to be operated upon

The third step in the cycle is to get the information that is stored at the address given in the instruction and then to cause the instruction to be performed by the proper part of the computer, typically the accumulator. When this operation is done the cycle is complete and the next heartbeat of the machine is started. Sometimes the third step is to store information instead of fetching it.

As a specific example, let us say there are these instructions:

instruction	meaning
CLA	*cl*ear and then *l*oad the *a*ccumulator
ADD	*add* to the accumulator
STO	*sto*re what is in the accumulator

Each instruction is followed by an address specifying where the information is to come from or go to. Suppose, then, that the current address register has (in binary, even though we give it in decimal) the address 1728, while in the locations in storage we have

location	instruction	address part
1728	CLA	X
1729	ADD	Y
1730	STO	Z

where, of course, X, Y, and Z are also addresses in the binary notation. In the first full cycle of three steps the machine will

1. read the current address register to get the address of the current instruction (which is 1728)
2. fetch the instruction from 1728 (which is CLA X)
3. clear out the accumulator and then load into it the contents of address X

For the second cycle (the current address register contents having been increased by 1), the control unit reads 1729. Therefore the control goes to location 1729 and finds the instruction ADD Y, which it obeys by adding the contents of Y to the number in the accumulator. During the third cycle the current address register contains the address 1730. The control then finds STO Z, which causes the machine to store the contents of the accumulator into location Z.

Let us remember that in fact the addresses we have labeled X, Y, and Z are sequences of binary digits and so are the CLA, ADD, and STO, since that is the form in which *all* information is stored in the machine. We have used the mnemonic labels so that the process can be followed more easily by humans.

The effect of these three instructions is to do the simple addition

$$Z = X + Y$$

meaning the number *in* X is added to the number *in* Y and the result is stored *in* Z, and in the model we are using it has consumed three complete cycles of machine activity.

CHANGES IN THE NORMAL SEQUENCE
OF CONTROL   4.4

The normal procedure of the usual computing machine is to get to successive instructions from consecutive addresses. However, it is a very important property of a computer that some of the instructions that the machine "knows" (can carry out) store numbers into the current address register, and others take numbers from the current address register and store them in the main storage unit.

The effect of storing a number into the current address register is that when the control goes to the current address register it does not find the number following the previous one, but instead it finds whatever number has been stored there. Thus there will be a break in the step-by-step process of going through storage to find successive instructions, and we transfer the control to some other place in the program of instructions. One particular use of this feature is that the machine can be caused to go back to a set of instructions that it earlier used and to repeat them again, perhaps on different numbers.

An instruction that stores the current address register contents into the main storage unit is also very useful. By using this instruction and then transfering the control to some other place in the program, we have the means of later finding our way back to where we were before we transfered the control, without our knowing exactly where in storage we were.

Among the instructions that store numbers into the current address register are some that do so *dependent upon what is in the accumulator*. Typically, one or more of the following five instructions may occur in a machine:

Store the address in the current address register (branch) if the number in the accumulator is

> greater than 0
> greater than or equal to 0
> equal to 0
> less than or equal to 0
> less than 0

These instructions are evidently what we use in coding our decision boxes of a flowchart.

Thus in many ways it is wrong to think of the arithmetic unit as a unit only for doing arithmetic. Rather, it is a general processor of binary sequences, and much of the power of the computer lies in this ability to change the path of the control as it goes through the storage unit using one instruction after another.

Because the repetition of parts of a program of instructions is so common, the engineers who design computers have supplied special units, called *index registers*, in the form of hardware to take over the counting of the number of times a loop of instuctions is to be traversed before branching out. In most modern machines index registers are used to carry out the details implied by an instruction like

DØ I = 0,2,30

which means the sequence of instructions that follows is to be done for the case I = 0, then step up the index I by 2 and do the sequence again, step up the index by 2 again and do the sequence again, ... , until the index has passed 30. Actually, such an instruction must also indicate precisely how many of the immediately following sequence of instructions is to be done. This is accomplished by giving the label of the last instruction of the loop. The form of the DØ instruction is therefore something like

DØ (down to) LABEL, I = 0,2,30

where LABEL is the label of some later instruction in the program. (The label is not the address of the instruction, though its ultimate effect is as if it were.)

There are four functions involving index registers:

1. The index register can be initially set.
2. The index register can be incremented (increased) or decremented by a fixed amount.
3. The index register's contents can be tested and possibly taken and used to do other things.
4. The contents of an index register are added, when called for, to the address of the instruction that is being fetched from storage. Thus the address where the instruction is to find its information is altered by the contents of some index register.

These two parts of the computer, the arithmetic unit and the index registers, are built to handle *numbers* (in binary notation). All the rest of the machine handles binary digits and has no special powers to process the binary digits as if they were binary numbers. Thus most of a computer is a binary-digit processor, and only these two special parts process binary numbers. That is, only they carry out processes that correspond to numerical operations.

INPUT AND OUTPUT (I/O)   4.5

It is obviously necessary to get information and processes (which are represented as binary digits and hence can also be called information) into and out of the machine. This is the function of the input and output units, abbreviated I/O. The input or the output information may be a deck of punched cards, a magnetic tape, a printer (output only), or any of a dozen other media.

I/O is a messy topic at best, and typically causes the user more trouble than all the rest of the machine put together. Part of the reason for this is that usually the I/O is very much slower than the central processor of the machine and therefore needs to be carefully managed if it is not to seriously limit the speed of the whole computation.

Because of the widely varying engineering details from machine to machine, and because it has little intellectual interest, we shall tend to ignore the topic. But please recognize that it can dominate the efficient use of machines in practice, and often a large degree of low cunning is required to handle it properly.

SYMBOLIC NOTATION, OR THE FIRST CHANGES
IN THE LANGUAGE   4.6

Since the machines are usually built of binary devices it is natural to
build them to process binary numbers rather than decimal numbers,
and also to use binary numbers for the addresses in the storage unit
itself. As we observed earlier, the binary system is *not* well adapted for
human use. The failure to match the machine design to the human
capabilities has led to an extensive evolution in how we actually run
machines, a history we now briefly recapitulate.

The problems of building the first machines were so great that the
engineers who built them made what they could in the simplest way
they could. It is no criticism of them to say that the machines were not
fit for humans to use since the humans were expected to communicate
with the machines in the binary notation.

Even before the machines were built, it was realized that we
would have to convert our decimal numbers to the machine's binary
equivalents and back, and that this would be an almost impossible
chore for humans to do. Therefore the task was put onto the machine
by the simple trick of writing special programs to do the converting.
Such programs are examples of *subroutines*. Let us describe a subroutine for carrying out this conversion. By storing

1. where the number to be converted were to be found
2. where the converted numbers were to be put
3. where the control was to go when the subroutine was done

and *then* transferring the control to the subroutine (by putting the first
address of the subroutine into the current address register) we "called
the subroutine." When the subroutine finished the job, the control
automatically returned to the place that was specified in (3) because
the subroutine placed the address from (3) into the current address
register. These, together with similar loading, punching, and printing
routines, were the earliest subroutines. Notice that the same subroutine
can be used repeatedly in the same or in different problems, since the
address of the data it operates on is passed to it by the program that
call it, as well as the address to return to when done.

By always using a formal way of calling subroutines, we introduce new elements into the language which are different from those given originally to the machine by the designers. To contrast this process with the hardware (the actual machine), programs of subroutines are called *software*. Small libraries of subroutines were gradually built up which, besides I/O and conversion routines, included square roots, sines, cosines, logs, exponentials, arctangents, and similar mathematical operations. These effectively add capabilities to the machine beyond those supplied by the hardware.

The trouble with the first library routines that were written was that in storage they tended to get in the way of each other and of the program that had already been written before the necessity of using a particular library routine was realized. This led to a method of *relocatable routines*. In this method routines do not have to be at any particular place in storage and will always work so long as the user knows where they are stored at the time he wants to use them.

Relocating a program in storage is not trivial. All instructions in the relocated program which refer to instructions or numbers in itself (and usually there are many of these) must have their addresses altered to the proper values for the current location of the library routine. By suitably writing the *loading program* and the library programs, this can be done at read-in time. In its day this was a great advance. Now we take it for granted, and do it easily and somewhat differently.

Each instruction like CLA is a sequence of more or less arbitrary 0s and 1s (arbitrary so far as the average human mind is concerned), and it is difficult to remember and write out the correct sequence when we want a particular instruction. The idea gradually emerged of using (as we have done) symbols like CLA to mean "clear and load accumulator" and having the machine at input time scan the incoming instructions, do a simple table lookup to find the equivalent string of 0s and 1s, and then have the machine insert them properly in the program in place of the CLA. This was the beginning of *symbolic coding*.

Once this was done, and well understood, it was possible to ask, "Why use the binary numbers, or any numbers for that matter, for the addresses? Why not use mnemonic names beginning with letters, as in the addresses?" The machine could clearly do what we had been doing by hand all the time and make up the table of equivalent names (in letters) and the actual addresses (in binary digits) at which *the machine chose* to store the numbers. We were therefore free to use names like

PAY   RATE   PI   LINE2   LINE6   SUM   PX7Q

for the names of the quantities rather than the actual numerical addresses where they were stored. An additional advantage was that the machine made the actual storage assignment at read-in time, and while we were preparing a program we were free to make all the changes we pleased without getting confused.

This process of putting the burden on the machine and taking it off the human is still going on. Of course, the effective ability of the machine is decreased in principle. But in fact so many errors are avoided that we get much more useful computation out of the same equipment by using these symbolic methods.

The power to give names to the machine operations soon suggested that we could give names to operations that the machine did not have. These were called *pseudo-operations* and we had the machine use suitable subroutines when these new operations occurred in the program.

The full-blown combination—that is, symbolic names for instructions and operands (addresses) and pseudo-operations—became known as an *assembler*. To write an assembler was once a great task for the expert, but now it is almost an exercise for the student. Assemblers are widely used today, indeed, what is often called *machine language* (also called *assembler language*) is usually one of these symbolic languages and is in fact far removed from the horrors of the real, absolute, binary coding that the machine actually uses when it is running.

The main further feature of an assembler is the macro-instruction, or *macro* for short, that enables the individual user to design his own pseudo-operations and have them automatically incorporated into the system at assembly time for his particular problem. Macros give the user the power to create almost a new language and then use it as he pleases.

COMPUTER NOTATION VERSUS
MATHEMATICAL NOTATION   4.7

When first seen, computer notation seems to be rather strange. It is, however, rather like mathematical notation in a different alphabet. In a single problem a mathematician may use v_c for the velocity of the car, and v_b for the velocity of the boat. Both symbols, though using one letter plus a subscript, are recognized as being a single quantity. When we came to copy the mathematical notation onto machines we were faced with the fact that the hardware we had, and were likely to get for some years to come, had only upper case alphabetic characters, plus the 10 decimal numbers and some assorted characters including some punctuation. We simply did not have subscripts and superscripts, let alone subscripts on the subscripts, and so on. Thus, if we were to have a large number of different symbols we would have to use something like the present system of creating symbols using up to, say, six characters, with the first one necessarily alphabetic. Some systems allow arbitrarily long names, but the advantage of the occasional long name to the human is frequently not worth the disadvantages to the machine.

The use of several letters for the name of a single quantity meant that the implied multiplication of the mathematician

xy (meaning x times y)

would have to be abandoned in practice and *all* multiplications would have to be specifically indicated. For this purpose the asterisk * was used. A * B is an example, SPEED * TIME is another.

Similarly, for powers such as

x^2

something else would have to be used because of the lack of superscripts. Conventionally, two asterisks in a row ** are used, thus

X ** 2 means x^2

Some systems use an "up arrow " ↑ instead of the double asterisk.

But the greatest logical difference is in the new use of the equality sign. In computing notation, a single name is used on the left of the equal sign and means that the quantity given on the right is to be the value of the name on the left, a replacement operator if you wish. Thus, as we earlier remarked, the equation

N = N + 1

means "take the value of N, add 1 to that value and now call that quantity N." (Store it in location N.)

The difference that most catches the eye of the outsider is the use of Ø for the letter O to distinguish it from the decimal digit 0. This tends to make the page look a bit strange, but it seems to be a matter of pride among beginners in computing: they use it even when it is not necessary.

NEW LANGUAGES   4.8

Section 4.6 showed how the machine language gradually evolved into an equivalent, slightly more powerful, but definitely more humane, language. Toward the end of this evolution it was clearly recognized that we were using and inventing languages for communication with machines. As a result of this insight the question arose of trying to copy the mathematical language directly.

The earliest and most famous attempt to use classical mathematical language was FORTRAN, an acronym for formula translation. If we may use the expression, this was evolution by mutation rather than evolution by small variation. The idea was that the FORTRAN language was to differ as little as possible from the conventional mathematical notation so that people would not have to learn a lot of new things to use computers. And it was probably more successful in doing this than even its inventors expected, for it has gone on through more than four versions. Each has been more powerful than the last, more powerful in the sense that more things could be said in the language, and each successive version has had more flexibility.

Many other special languages have been devised. For business applications, the language COBOL was developed (common business oriented language) at the specific request of the Department of Defense. COMIT for work in linguistics, LISP for list structures, and ALGOL (an international effort at an algorithmic language for mathematics which the inventors hoped would replace FORTRAN but which did not in this country) are other examples.

Given a special field of application, often the first step is to devise a language that describes the basic quantities and processes of the field. If there is a unique way of going from this language to machine language, then a translator is made. With this translator available, problems in the field can be written in the new language and run on the machine *after* first running through the translation process to get the translated program.

Where the translation is completely done *before* the problem is run, the program that does it is called a *compiler*. But where the translation is done as it is needed (word for word, as it were), it is called an *interpreter*. The advantage of the compiler is that the translation need be done only once. On the other hand, each time the program comes to an instruction (perhaps in going around a loop), the interpreter has to translate the instruction again. The advantage of the interpreter is that when trouble occurs, the machine is very close to the language the human used, so that in reporting the trouble it is easy to give useful information to the user. A compiled program is, at the moment of trouble, far from the original language, and to help the human the translation must have contained a lot of redundant information to indicate the trouble in the original language.

There are subtle logical differences between compiling and interpreting. There are economic differences as well, but we will not go into them here.

A SIMPLE INTERPRETER 4.9

The idea of using a language for communicating with a computer that is different from the language given by the machine designer is basic to the use of computers in practice. We can illustrate this by a simple example. In a sense we shall be simulating one machine on another machine.

Suppose that a given computing machine has a language of the form

Operation | Address of operand

with operations like

CLA	X	clear and load the accumulator with the contents of X
ADD	X	add the contents of X to what is now in the accumulator
STO	X	store the contents of the accumulator into location X
MPY	X	multiply what is in the accumulator by the number in location X
TRA	X	transfer control to location X

In each case the following address is the location (the source) of the number, where the answer is to go, or where control is to go next.

Suppose now that we wish to simulate a machine having a language of the form:

Ø	A	B	C
x	xxx	xxx	xxx

where Ø is the operation, and A, B, and C are the addresses of the three operands, each given by a 3-digit decimal number. The operations are as follows:

operation	meaning
1	add
2	subtract
3	multiply
4	divide

and so on, for all the instructions of the machine to be simulated.

Thus the instruction 1 347 732 556 means, "Add the number stored at location 347 to the number stored at location 732 and put the result in location 556."

Suppose further that the machine we are using has 2000 registers, numbered 0000 to 1999. We will be able to refer only to locations 0000 to 0999 because the machine to be simulated uses 3 decimal digits for each address. Thus we imagine that the program of our interpreter will be stored in the upper 1000 registers, while the program to be interpreted will be in the lower 1000 registers.

We need to assign a *current address register* for our simulation of a machine. Suppose it to be location 1234. We make the following use of the upper 1000 addresses, as shown in Figure 4-2.

Our interpreter program (Figure 4-3) that simulates our three-address machine begins by picking up the number from address 1234 which tells where the next instruction of our three-address program— sometimes called the *object program*—is located. It then adds this number to a CLA with 0000 address to obtain a CLA Oxxx instruction. We then obey this machine-language instruction we have just created to get the three-address simulated instruction into the accumulator. Here we dissect the simulated instruction, using the logical and shift instructions, and we then store the addresses A, B, and C (properly

storage register	contents
1100	start of subroutine for ADD
1200	start of subroutine for SUBT
1234	current address register
1235	A
1236	B
1237	C
1300	start of subroutine for MULT
1400	start of subroutine for DIVIDE

Figure 4-2

shifted left or right) in standard places, which we will choose to be locations 1235, 1236, 1237. Next we take the instruction digit x, shift it to the hundreds position, and add the instruction TRA 1000 to it, obtaining TRA 1x00. We now execute this machine-language instruction, which transfers control to the first location of a subroutine that performs the corresponding operation. (The subroutines have been carefully placed in locations 1100, 1200, and so on, so this works out properly.)

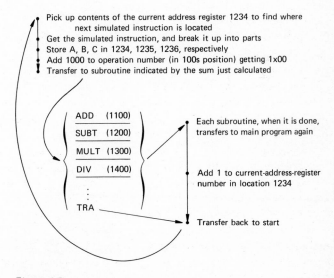

Pick up contents of the current address register 1234 to find where next simulated instruction is located
Get the simulated instruction, and break it up into parts
Store A, B, C in 1234, 1235, 1236, respectively
Add 1000 to operation number (in 100s position) getting 1x00
Transfer to subroutine indicated by the sum just calculated

ADD (1100)
SUBT (1200)
MULT (1300)
DIV (1400)
⋮
TRA

Each subroutine, when it is done, transfers to main program again

Add 1 to current-address-register number in location 1234

Transfer back to start

Figure 4-3

Let us consider the operation ADD (see Figure 4-4) and examine how the subroutine to perform addition will have to appear. It will end with the four instructions stored in locations 1120-1123:

```
1120    CLA  A
1121    ADD  B
1122    STO  C
1123    TRA to main program
```

The first three of these, at the moment, are blank. We will have to get these instructions from inside the routine for ADD and, one by one, add to them the contents of locations 1225, 1226, 1227, which are

	address	instruc-tions	address	
	1100	CLA	1235	create instruction in 1120
	1101	ADD	1125	
	1102	STO	1120	
	1103	CLA	1236	create instruction in 1121
These set the program up	1104	ADD	1126	
	1105	STO	1121	
	1106	CLA	1237	create instruction in 1122
	1107	ADD	1127	
	1108	STO	1222	
	1109	TRA	1120	
These three instructions actually do the operation to be simulated	1120	Blank		ending block of instructions
	1121	Blank		
	1122	Blank		
Return	1123	TRA	to main program	
	1125	CLA	0000	"constants" needed by program
	1126	ADD	0000	
	1127	STO	0000	

Figure 4-4   ADD routine.

where A, B, and C are stored. We can then actually perform these three constructed instructions and finally execute a TRA that takes us back to the main program again. If you carefully follow the instructions in Figure 4-4 you will see how this is accomplished.

Each of the arithmetic (and other) subroutines have the same general structure. They construct the appropriate instructions, execute them, and transfer back to the main program again. The main program (see Figure 4-3) adds 1 to the simulated current address register and loops back again to pick up the next simulated instruction, dissects it, transfers to the appropriate subroutine, and so on. The transfer type of instructions transfer control to a point *beyond* the instructions that add 1 to the current address register so that the main program will pick up the proper new simulated instruction.

Thus we see that we have simulated one machine having one instruction language on another machine with a quite different language. This is common these days. When a computing machine is being designed it is very useful to simulate the way the instructions will work together as a group to see whether or not they form a good combination for a language. Later, when an assembler program must be writtern for the new machine, it can also be tested using the same simulator. Finally, when the prospective customer for the new machine wants to prepare his programs, he can use the assembler, together with the simulator, on his old machine. The manufacture of simulators has reached a high degree of development because of their great utility.

One side effect of the growth of simulators is the *emulator*, a combination of software and hardware that enables a manufacturer of machines to offer a machine that is compatible with other machines. In an emulator, much of the interpretation of instructions is performed by hardware instead of software.

If we were building a compiler rather than an interpreter, we would put the constructed instructions out on a suitable storage mechanism rather than executing them immediately. When we later read the output back in we would have a program ready to run. We have glossed over some small differences, but the ideas should be clear.

FURTHER REMARKS ON COMPILERS 4.10

If we have a symbolic language with a wide range of possible names we will find ourselves in the position of the hotelkeeper in Section 3.7 We have symbolic names appearing continually and need to know what actual locations are being used. The method of hash tables of Chapter 3 meets this need very well and avoids comparing the name at hand with the whole list of names that have been assigned addresses.

In operation, a compiler usually causes an expansion of the number of instructions. Indeed, in some respects, the more machine instructions produced from one instuction in the problem language, the more powerful the language. Roughly speaking, the human writes less but gets more for the same effort—which is what we want.

SUMMARY   4.11

The computer uses both information and descriptions of processes represented as sequences of 0s and 1s. The arithmetic unit and index registers have special arithmetical properties, but fundamentally the machine uses only strings of 0s and 1s. Furthermore, although we have been clever and caused the machine to look like some other machine with very different properties, the machine basically does "absolute-binary instructions" only. All the rest is only appearance, but the appearance is a much more humane machine. We have also shown how a machine can be made to act as if it were designed to use a language that was not "designed into" the hardware of the machine. This is an important concept and reveals some of the power of a general-purpose computer.

CHAPTER 5

Schickard Calculator (Wilhelm Schickard, 1592-1635)
From a replica in the IBM Corporation Antique Calculator Collection.

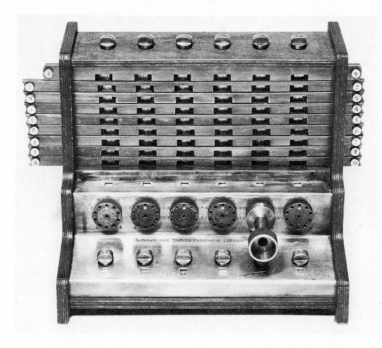

We have already examined briefly the logical process of planning a

5

Examples from Geometry

We have already examined briefly the logical process of planning a problem. In this and the next chapter we shall present some idea of what happens in actual practice.

Unfortunately, realistic problems are much too large and complex to be used to introduce the topic of problem planning. Typically, a large problem will involve 1 to 10 or even 100 man-years of work, and thousands to hundreds of thousands of instructions in the final program. We must be content to look at trivial, hypothetical examples. The examples that follow have been chosen to illustrate some of the ideas and things that can happen in practice without getting involved in the true complexity of real problems. Thus it is admittedly an artificial presentation, and an artificial style is used to give the flavor of reality. You are expected to use your imagination to scale these problems up to reality.

THE FIRST PROBLEM: CLASSIFYING TRIANGLES   **5.1**

Suppose you are given many sets of three numbers, A, B, C, where each set is said to be the lengths of the sides of a triangle. The problem is to classify the triangles as

scalene	no two sides of the same length
isosceles	two sides of equal length
equilateral	three sides of the same length,

and also classify the triangles as

acute	no angle as large as a right angle
right	one angle is a right angle
obtuse	one angle greater than a right angle

The problem appears to be so simple that we quickly draw a pair of boxes (Figure 5-1), the first doing the first classification, the second box doing the second classification.

In most problems it is necessary to use some technical information to supply the details in the next stage of the flowchart expansion process, and this usually comes from the field of application—in this case, geometry. As to the technical details we need to know, for the

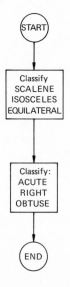

Figure 5-1

first box it is trivial as they follow from the definitions, and for the second box we need Pythagoras's theorem, which states that for a right triangle the sum of the squares of the two sides equals the square of the hypotenuse. We appear to be well on our way to a more detailed flowchart and no trouble is in sight.

A Hidden Assumption

It was completely unstated, but there was a tacit assumption that the three sides did form a triangle. But do they? Should we say that the numbers 2, 4, 9 correspond to a scalene triangle because no two sides are equal? No, because they simply do not form a triangle. We had better check this first! Thus there must be a third box, a box that precedes the two we had, one which examines whether or not there is a triangle. The technical information that we need from geometry this time is that the sum of any two sides of a triangle must be greater than the third side.

To summarize what has happened up to this point, we were given a reasonable-sounding problem and started to do it, but a little thought showed that *part of the problem had not even been stated*. When we did state it, we found that besides the two pieces of information from the technical background of the problem (geometry), we needed another piece of technical information, namely, a criterion for deciding whether there was or was not a triangle. This is very characteristic of real situations. (1) The given statements are not adequate, or some things have been completely overlooked, and (2) to solve the problem, we need various pieces of technical information from the background field of the problem. At this point our flowchart has three boxes (Figure 5-2).

Expansion of the Flowchart

It is traditional at this stage to farm out the various boxes to different people, telling them to get together and agree on the interfaces, namely, the notation and names used to describe what they are doing. This is one of the many dangerous steps in programming a problem for machine solution. Instead, we ourselves shall mull over the three stages a bit to see what they might look like before we go ahead and complete the job.

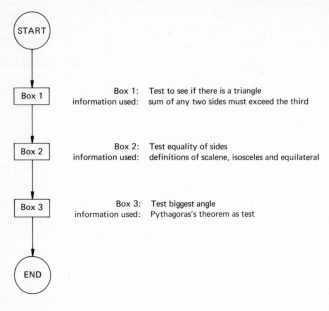

Box 1:   Test to see if there is a triangle
information used: sum of any two sides must exceed the third

Box 2:   Test equality of sides
information used: definitions of scalene, isosceles and equilateral

Box 3:   Test biggest angle
information used: Pythagoras's theorem as test

Figure 5-2

In the first box we will have to compare the sum of two sides with the third *three different times* to check it completely. Further, we will have to decide about equality. Did we really want to say "greater than," or would "greater than or equal to" be more appropriate? Is 2, 5, 7 a triangle? I know that the statement was "greater than," and that a dictionary or an elementary mathematics book would very likely rule out the equality, but I have learned from experience to go to the man who was going to use the results and check with him. Only he can know what is wanted, and no textbook, mathematician, or dictionary can settle it. True, we could be logical and say we solved the problem just as it was asked, but long experience shows the wisdom of checking to find out if the original statement was as carefully considered as it should have been. There is little sense in doing the wrong problem perfectly.

In the second box we will compare pairs of sides two at a time, three trials in all, to see if the triangle is isosceles. Of course, if the first two are equal, we need go no further and can exclude the scalene at once. And if the first two sides are equal, we need to compare only one of them with the third to see if it is an equilateral triangle. Again, a degenerate case arises if we accept a triangle of side 0. Is, for example, 6, 6, 0 an isosceles triangle? And if it is taken to be the limit as one side approaches zero, how are we going to handle the triangle 0, 0, 0? It could be the limit of any-shaped triangle as all the sides approach zero proportionally. Well, we had best consult the user of the results again for *another* ruling on this same sticky point. Suppose, to be specific, it is decided to exclude sides of length 0.

In the third box we will have to figure out which two of the sides are to be squared and added and then compared with the remaining side squared. If the sum is less, then we have obtuse. If equal, we have right. And if greater, we have acute. But wait a moment! What do we mean by equal? Yes, it is obvious if we have nice integer lengths like 3, 4, and 5, or 5, 12, and 13. But suppose we had the sides from the mathematically exact right triangle 1, 1, $\sqrt{2}$. The number representing the $\sqrt{2}$ will be only approximately represented in the machine, and the square will not be exactly 2. Apparently a small amount should be left for this roundoff error. But suppose the sides were 1000, 1000, $1000\sqrt{2}$. The error will be 1000 times larger—while if we had 1/1000, 1/1000, $\sqrt{2}/1000$ it would be very small. In the latter case, *any* triangle of that general size might well pass as a right triangle when in fact it was very far from it. It is clear, now, that we will have to adopt some criterion of error based on the size of the difference *relative* to say, the largest side. So again we have to think of details and ask questions that were not thought of in the earlier stages, and quite likely we must again *seek guidance* from the man who is going to use the results as to what is or is not to be accepted as a right triangle.

Another Revision of the Problem

Because we have ourselves examined, even slightly, the whole problem and noticed that in each part there is going to be a lot of shuffling around of the trials to try all possible combinations, we begin to suspect that maybe some of this can be done once and for all rather than repeatedly.

We are unable to explain how the idea occurred, but it did suddenly seem clear that if we added another box, *before* everything else, in which we sorted the given lengths in order, so that we had A $\leqslant$ B $\leqslant$ C, where A, B, C are the lengths of the sides, we might gain a lot.

Just what do we gain? In the first test, to see if there is a triangle or not, we now need to make only one trial, namely $A + B > C$ (we exclude equal), because the other two tests are automatically true. In the second box we need to try only the equality of $A = B$, and then $B = C$ for the equilateral, isosceles, or scalene test. In the third box, for right triangles, we have that automatically if there is a right triangle then A and B are the legs, and C must be the hypotenuse. Again, only one arrangement of the sides need be tested. It looks as if the sorting will pay!

Notice that probably no person programming only a single box could have afforded to do the sorting job. And even if he did, unless

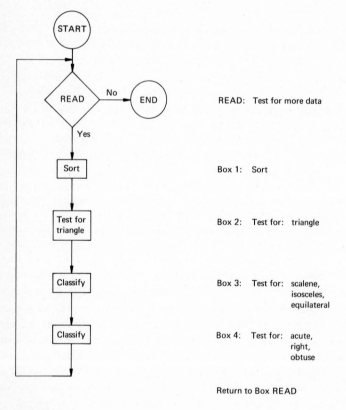

Figure 5-3

this detail were specifically told to the others, they would not have profited by it. Only because the *whole* of the problem was kept in one mind did the possibility for the rearrangement of the problem occur, as well as the possible consequent savings in coding detail and in the machine time used, and the much greater clarity of the whole process.

We also finally recall that we are not writing so elaborate a program merely to classify one set of three lengths. Implicit in the work is that there will be many sets and we had best include this in the problem. Not knowing the actual number of sets, we can use the READ to see if more cases are to be processed or if we are done. Thus we now recognize that we have a loop in the program (see Figure 5-3).

One thing that has been suppressed up to this point is that, in fact, a fair number of imagined sets of lengths have been tried at various stages of thought, often almost casually, to see what was likely to happen. Based on long experience, very extreme cases were automatically tried to see what would happen. For example, what will happen if some or all of the lengths given are negative numbers? *Of course* you thought that they should be positive, but suppose some nut is getting the lengths from the map and he is measuring one side in the South direction and one in the West. Isn't it all too possible that the fool (of course *we* wouldn't) would give negative lengths? We leave this as an exercise to the reader to see what modifications, if any, would be necessary to handle this.

Making the More Detailed Flowchart

The READ box must test for the presence or absence of more data and *should* print the three numbers that are read in so that we have some identification of the results from the rest of the diagram.

The first box to be drawn in more detail is that for sorting the three given numbers A, B, C, into order so that we have $A \leqslant B \leqslant C$. (Note that because of the sorting, we may have changed the names of sides we were given and assigned new names A, B, C to some sequence of the old numbers A, B, C, rather than keep the old or invent completely new names—a typical trick used in programming and one that can confuse the unwary.) Sorting is one of the most difficult processes in computing. For three numbers it is easy to find a method: compare adjacent numbers, and if they are not in order, then interchange the pair and go on to test the next pair, repeating this until

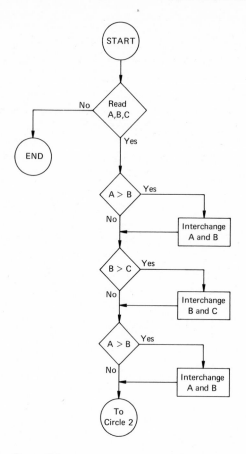

Figure 5-4

every pair is in order. Note that when you first tested a pair they may have been in order, but later one of them may have been changed by some other comparison, and you have to do it again. A flowchart to do this part is shown in Figure 5-4.

Does this flowchart really work in all cases? How can we tell? The traditional way is to make up some numbers and try acting like the machine to see what happens. No amount of this will *prove* that all cases will work (unless you are prepared to try all cases!), but a careful choice of trials, together with the use of imagination, will often convince you that the plan is probably correct. Let us try some sets of data. Suppose we have

A	B	C
5	7	3

Writing down what happens line by line, we get to the end of the diagram having done the following:

Another set of data might be

What is the worst input data that could happen for the process? Isn't it likely that the worst case occurs when the lengths are completely in reverse order? Therefore we finally try

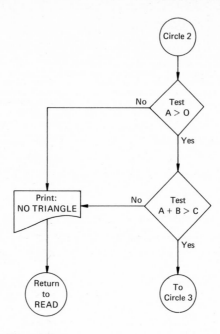

Figure 5-5

It seems we have the first box (sorting) under control. Let us turn to the next box.

In the second box we are to test for a triangle. We have the ruling that if one side is zero, it is not a triangle. In expanding the second box we therefore first test the smallest side A (now that the sorting is done) to see if it is greater than zero. This automatically also detects negative lengths. (Hadn't we better check the sorting routine for negative numbers?) It only remains to test $A + B > C$ and to reject the case as not being a triangle if it is not true. The result is again printed so that the user can know what the machine decided.

Notice we have created a new loop on the diagram (Figure 5-5), going from "no triangle" back to READ again, something we casually overlooked at the earlier stages. There is hardly any point in trying data for this simple calculation.

The expansion of the third box requires a sequence of tests, all of which are fairly obvious (see Figure 5-6). We need to ask ourselves if the three tests shown are all needed, or if it is possible to get by with two. After a bit of consideration, we decide that it is not obvious that two are sufficient. So we keep all three, although only two are used for any one set of data. Again, to test the effectiveness of the flowchart, we try various sets of data and act like the machine in following out the diagram. We leave it to the reader to test it, using suitable sets of data.

The expansion of the fourth box (see Figure 5-7) needs a separate number for the input, namely, the tolerance from exact equality that will be permitted in testing for a right triangle. Let us suppose that this number is called E and that it has been specified, either as an input number before any sets of sides were given, or else as a number permanently stored in this program for use on all problems that use this block. We first compute the relative error R which measures how far the data is from being a right triangle. The test for a right triangle follows, and then the further classification.

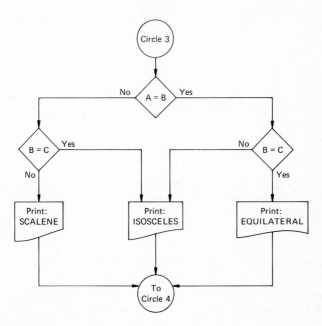

Figure 5-6

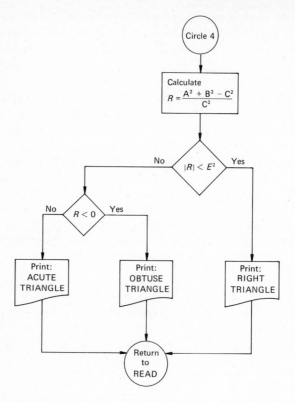

Figure 5-7

To check the acute-obtuse test we assume a reasonable E and try first a known acute triangle, say, 1, 1, 1, and then a known obtuse triangle, say, 3, 4, 6.

Notice that we have been careful at each stage to print out the results. Often the beginner, and occasionally the expert, gets so involved in the process of making the machine do the proper things that he forgets to have the machine report out what has happened so that the human can find out. It is important to see that the output will be readable. We have as our output:

the three lengths, A, B, C, in the original order
the rejection NO TRIANGLE if appropriate
one of three: SCALENE, ISOSCELES, or EQUILATERAL
one of three: ACUTE, RIGHT, or OBTUSE

As we noted earlier, the problem would never have been to do the job for one set, but would be used over and over again. In the application we imagined, many sets of three lengths were to be classified, so the flowchart would loop back to the READ statement for more data. In more complex situations this program might be only a part (a sub-routine) of a larger program, and control would get back again only through other parts of the larger program.

EXERCISES—5.1*a*

1. Make a flowchart to sort four numbers A, B, C, D into *decreasing* order.

2. Make a flowchart to compute the diagonal of a three-dimensional rectangular box of sides $x, y, z,$.

What Have We Learned?

Some of the points to be emphasized in this example are these:

1. We learned how different the problem becomes from that given originally, in particular because of the hidden assumptions. This is very characteristic of real problems. Rarely does a reasonably large problem occur in which this does not happen one or more times. Even experts must watch for this

2. The plan was almost completely revised. When we gradually saw the amount of shuffling that was going to be needed, the inclusion of the sorting greatly simplified the thinking and the later work. But this change arose *only* because someone looked at the entire problem in considerable detail.

3. The need for a great deal of technical information from the field of application (geometry, in our case) is very characteristic of problem solving on a computer.

4. There is need to get specific decisions from the user of the results about treatment of the special and degenerate cases. This is one of the most common failures in computing. The wrong problem is elegantly solved, and it is practically impossible to find out that it is the wrong problem.

5. There are a great number of seemingly trivial details and small decisions to be made, and all of them must be given to the machine. This is where much of the time goes, time that seems to the outsider to be wasted.

6. Remember the simple trick of inventing data and then acting like the machine to see if the instructions are actually as you intended them to be. This is a very powerful tool.

7. We noted the practical impossibility of being *absolutely sure* that the program is correct and that everything has been foreseen.

8. We saw the usefulness of the flowchart in ordering one's thoughts and helping to break down complex situations into simple ones. It is amazing to see what sometimes appears to be an impossibly complex situation yield to the method. It is also amazing to see some apparently simple situations that do not!

9. If all this can happen on a trivial problem, consider what can happen in actual practice on a large problem.

EXERCISES—5.1*b*

3. Given four lengths A, B, C, D forming a convex quadrilateral (four-sided figure with no dents), make a flowchart for classifying the quadrilateral as having opposite sides parallel. Also, classify as a rhomboid (all four sides of equal length).

4. Draw the detailed flowchart for a box classifying the triangles as scalene, isosceles, and equilateral if the numbers are not sorted.

5. Same as Exercise 4 for the box classifying as right triangle.

6. Given six numbers that are lengths, will they form a tetrahedron? Make a flowchart to test them.

THE SECOND PROBLEM: CIRCUMSCRIBED
REGULAR POLYGONS   5.2

Suppose we start with a circle of radius 1 (1 inch, or 1 foot, or 1 mile), and we draw around it an equilateral triangle (circumscribed triangle), and around the triangle we draw another circle. Around this circle we draw a square, and around the square we draw another circle. Then we draw a regular five-sided polygon and another circle, then a regular six-sided polygon and a circle, and so on, continuing indefinitely (Figure 5-8). How will the radii of the circles behave? Will they approach infinity (get arbitrarily large), or will they remain bounded by some finite size?

Here we have a problem that is not hard to state or to under-

Figure 5-8

stand, but for a nonmathematician it is difficult to decide what will happen to the radius of the circle as we go farther and farther along the sequence. One way to get a better idea of what is happening is to calculate the successive radii and examine the growth of the numbers. Perhaps from examining the numbers we can make up our minds as to how to answer the question.

This situation is very typical of what happens in research: we use the computer, not to get a definite answer, but rather to get a feel for the problem. From the computed results we hope to grasp the general pattern of whatever we are examining. Thus the machine is used as an experimental tool much as one would use a laboratory.

We could calculate the radii of the first few circles by hand and they might indicate a pattern, but on the other hand, even 10 answers would hardly convince us as to the behavior in the long run. What we are likely to need, and we cannot be sure now just how many, seems to be a few hundred or so. We need to analyze, therefore, how to go from one radius to the next one.

One of the best ways of getting started in many mathematical problems is to set up a notation. Be ready to abandon it later if necessary. Clearly we need a notation for the radii of the various circles. We are tempted to use $R(0)$ for the initial radius, but because we are starting out with a triangle, maybe we should call the radius of the given first circle $R(2)$. Around this circle we draw the triangle, and then the radius of the circle around the triangle is called $R(3)$. We draw the square around this and the radius of the circle around the square is

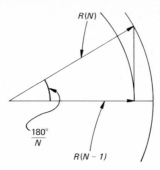

Figure 5-9

$R(4)$. In general, around the circle of radius $R(N)$ we draw a regular polygon of $N + 1$ sides, and around this polygon we draw the circle of radius $R(N + 1)$. Thus we start with $R(2) = 1$.

To find $R(N)$ we suppose we have the previous radius $R(N - 1)$. Around this circle we put an N-sided regular polygon. Let us look at a picture of the situation (Figure 5-9), another very powerful trick in solving mathematical problems. We look at one side of the regular polygon only. From the picture (which is said to be worth a thousand words) we see, after some thought, that we have a right triangle with two sides $R(N)$ and $R(N - 1)$ with a known angle $180°/N$ between the two sides. If this is not clear to you, review the requirements of the problem by making a sketch of what was described in words in the first paragraph of this section.

We now dredge up from memory a fragment of trigonometry and recall that

$$\frac{R(N - 1)}{R(N)} = \cos(180°/N)$$

This is the key piece of technical information that is needed. As is so often the case, it comes from the particular field of application. We rewrite this equation in the more convenient form

$$R(N) = \frac{R(N - 1)}{\cos(180°/N)}$$

That is, to get the next radius after the polygon of N sides we take the previous radius $R(N-1)$ and divide by $\cos(180°/N)$.

We can compute the first few cases explicitly.

$$R(3) = \frac{R(2)}{\cos 60°} = \frac{1}{1/2} = 2$$

$$R(4) = \frac{R(3)}{\cos 45°} = \frac{2}{1/\sqrt{2}} = 2\sqrt{2} = 2.828\ldots$$

$$R(5) = \frac{R(4)}{\cos 36°} = \frac{2.828\ldots}{0.809} \cong 3.496\ldots$$

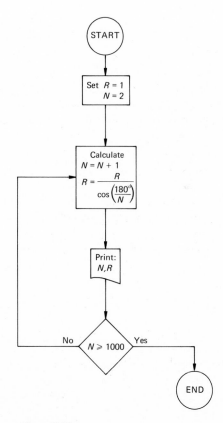

Figure 5-10

However, we want a program to compute the numbers for us and thus we need a flowchart (see Figure 5-10). In the computation we need one location in storage for the radius and one for where we are in the sequence. Thus we need $R(N)$ and N. We initialize the problem by setting $N = 2$ and $R(2) = 1$. Now we have a loop (with a print order so we can see the results) for computing the next case and a decision for stopping.

As usual, we check the program by simulating the machine for a few steps and compare our results with those we did by hand. We gloss over the practical difficulties of printing, since the thousand lines would be painful to print, and we simply present an abbreviated table of results (Table 5.2-1).

Table 5.2-1

N	R	N	R	N	R	N	R
3	2.0000	20	6.8369	200	8.4885	10,000	8.6959
4	2.8284	30	7.3997	300	8.5583	20,000	8.6981
5	3.4961	40	7.7017	400	8.5935	30,000	8.6993
6	4.0370	50	7.8900	500	8.6146	50,000	8.6996
7	4.4807	60	8.0184	600	8.6288	100,000	8.6996
8	4.8499	70	8.1118	700	8.6389	200,000	8.6996
9	5.1611	80	8.1826	800	8.6465		
10	5.2467	90	8.2383	900	8.6524		
		100	8.2831	1000	8.6572		

After considering the table, can we now answer the question? Does it seem as if R is approaching infinity (growing larger than any fixed number you state in advance), or does it seem likely to be bounded by something less than 9.0000, or perhaps even by 8.7000?

Implications

We have already commented on the fact that this problem typifies the use of machines to explore complicated situations which seem to be too difficult to get through by pure thought (or at least it would be too much work for a nonmathematically trained person to think it through). Actually, another reason for computing is that while you may, by thinking hard, be able to convince yourself about the behavior of the numbers, you may still have a great deal of trouble convincing others of your beliefs. With a table of numbers it is much easier to get them to see why you are right. Note that this *does not prove* that the radius is bounded. It is merely very suggestive that it is, and would very likely convince you enough to bet money on it, and such is the case in most real engineering situations. In life, action must almost always be taken without any guaranteed proof that the actions will result in what you want. Indeed, one is often not even sure that the problem is stated correctly, yet action must be taken. In such situations the computer is often a great comfort and consolation, since you can simulate complex situations with it and see how things come out.

SUMMARY   **5.3**

We have looked at two quite different problems in geometry. The purpose of the first was to show how many details and hidden assumptions are apt to lie in even a simple problem. By inference, there are many more in larger, more realistic problems. We also emphasized two points: first, it is the user of the results who should control the way the many details are handled, and second, in all problems it is necessary to have some technical knowledge from the field of application to use the computer properly. It is unrealistic to suppose that professional programmers know such things, and therefore their work must be closely monitored if nonsense is not to emerge on the nicely printed pages.

The purpose of the second problem was to show how machines are used in a more creative way to help the mind, rather than, as in the first case, the machine being used to help the person do routine work.

CHAPTER 6

Pascal's Computing Machine (Blaise Pascal, 1623-1662)
From the original in the IBM Corporation Antique Calculator Collection.

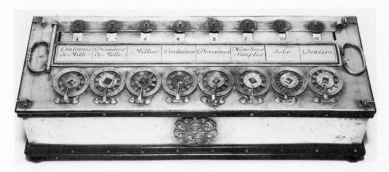

6

Examples from Business

In almost every area of computer application it is necessary to have the appropriate technical background if the situation is to be examined in any detail. In Chapter 5 the problems came from geometry. Business provides another set of applications. The main technical knowledge needed in business is, of course, accounting, a subject that many know superficially but few understand in depth. We shall choose our business examples to avoid using much detailed accounting. But the point should be clear. We have chosen the fields because they are generally known to the average person, not because of any inherent interest (or noninterest) in them. The applications should be thought of only as typical of a much wider class of problems in which computers can be and are used.

The need for technical knowledge in the field of application being obvious to us now, it follows that the more you know about a field, the better you are able to use computers in that field. But it should also be made clear that *the way you go about doing a problem by hand and the way you go about it by machine are apt to be very different.* Many of the failures in the application of computers in the past have been due to the neglect of this simple rule—it is all too often forgotten. The situation is similar to that of mass production, where one does not make exactly the same product as was made by hand but some equivalent item. For example, hand methods tend to favor screws and nuts and bolts as fasteners, while mass production lines tend to use riveting and spot welding. In a similar way, computer accounting is likely to be different from hand methods.

Of all technical backgrounds, mathematics is generally the most helpful when considering a wide range of applications. It is probably the most useful single language for communicating with machines. We shall have to use it on many occasions, and Section 6.5 will discuss some of its uses in more detail.

We are confined to simple, easily followed examples. Their purpose is to illustrate how problems are done and not how business is run.

A SIMPLE PAYROLL EXAMPLE   6.1

One of the most common and earliest applications of computers to business is the problem of making up the payroll. The basic idea is simple. We imagine that we have a table of names (more likely payroll *numbers*) and rates of pay. At a given time in the weekly cycle of accounting, time cards are collected. The time cards record the time the person has worked on the various activities of the company. Often the total of hours worked is included, though the machine can easily compute this.

Suppose we have the simple rule that overtime is paid at the rate of time and a half whenever the person works over 40 hours—and all we care about at the moment is paying the employee. The flowchart is then easy to prepare (Figure 6-1). We read in the time card, compute the total hours, and check to see if the total is over 40 hours. If it is, then we multiply the amount over 40 by 3/2 and add 40. If it is 40 or less we leave it as it stands. Next, we get the rate of pay from the table of names (if payroll numbers are used as identification, we also get the name so that we can print it on the paycheck later). We then multiply the effective number of hours by the rate of pay to compute the amount of the paycheck. Then we go back and read the next time card and repeat the process.

Now let us consider some more details. What about Federal income tax deductions? Well, it will take a box of coding that, as anyone who ever prepared an income tax form well knows, will require

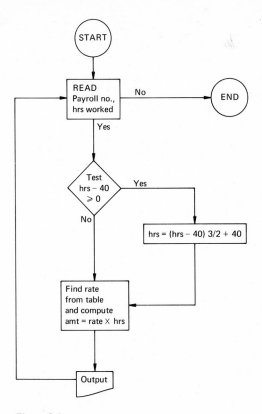

Figure 6-1

much detailed study, care, and planning to get right. And then there is Social Security to be treated, and state income tax, and special company-sponsored group insurance withholding, government bond purchases, possibly stock purchases, cash advances, and so on. The company may be located in one state, the person for whom the check is being computed lives in another state, and during the week he moved to a third state. Each will take a smaller or larger box of coding. When you consider all the other messy complications that can arise in practice (including the obvious one in which the total deductions exceed the amount earned), perhaps it can be realized why a program for doing a simple payroll may take several man-years of effort to prepare. Even then most of the time is not spent in doing the actual coding but in trying to find out what the rules are.

There are at least two traps waiting for the unwary person attempting a payroll program. First, he is apt not to realize that there will be many exceptions to be handled and that the program must be written to handle most of them automatically—every exception cannot be rejected by the machine and left to hand calculations. The second trap is exactly opposite: so many possible exceptions might occur (but usually do not) that to prepare a program to cover each one is prohibitively expensive. Several early payroll programs came to grief over the second error. What should be done is to cover almost all of the cases most likely to occur in the next year or two. Those that are not likely to occur should not be covered. You might object by saying you cannot know what is going to happen next year. That is true and obvious but also irrelevant. You have to do the best you can, and that is one of the things that makes the big difference between a good payroll program and a poor one.

BATCH VERSUS CONTINUOUS PROCESSING   6.2

The payroll program just described was a *batch process* program. At a given time all the payroll cards are collected and then processed one after another. The idea is that batch processing is necessary to meet outside requirements (such as a fixed payday) as well as internal efficiency. But there is another side to the problem that occurs sooner or later. As an example of what can happen, consider a friend of mine from India whose father died suddenly. My friend wished, naturally, to return to India immediately. But the Federal government has a rule: it will not permit a foreigner to leave the country until it is sure, among other things, that he has paid all his income taxes. The means, in effect, that the company he works for must prepare his paycheck in final detail at almost a moment's notice, and it cannot wait until the usual period in the week to do so.

This is typical of one side condition of the payroll program, and others also. While conceptually payroll programs are run as a batch process, they must permit breaking into at almost random times to complete one or more special cases. They must take on some of the characteristics of a continuous process accounting system. An airline reservation system is an extreme example of processing with transactions occurring at unpredictable times. It functions by a moment-to-moment updating of the reservations, and it must be prepared to give details at any time before, or even after, flight time. A recent frill that checks to see that the same person is not trying to make multiple reservations on the same day to the same place (if he is, it automatically cancels *both* reservations) requires that not only the single flight be consulted, but also a whole class of other flights on other airlines, some having intermediate stops not given on the first flight.

The subtleties of making an apparent batch processing program cope with occasional special requests are more than can be discussed here. But the point has been raised to indicate again that although the general way a machine can be made to do a problem may be easy to understand, in most situations there is a large mass of specialized knowledge required for doing a good job. Also necessary is considerable skill in the art of clear thinking.

An example of good planning came to the attention of the author some years ago. A company was faced with a strike. After the strike the workers went back to work with the understanding that all pay raises and other changes in the union contract were to be retroactive to a given date. As the negotiations went on, more and more promotions, deaths, and changes in personnel occurred, all of which had to be corrected at some later date not then known. The structure of the system withstood the shock of the sudden unforeseen demand very well. The reason it did so was that the brain behind the initial planning had organized the whole into a broad, comprehensive, sensible plan and had neither taken ad hoc steps nor cut corners in the execution of this general plan.

INVENTORY PROBLEMS 6.3

Another common type of business application of computers is the inventory problem. In a sense the airline reservation system can be considered an inventory problem. At the beginning of the day the system starts with a number of available seats on various flights. During the day there are withdrawals (reservations) made, requests that cannot be met (no more available seats on that flight), and returns to stock (canceled reservations).

Whether the inventory is kept on a moment-to-moment (continuous) or day-to-day (batch) basis depends on the requirements of the system. More elaborate systems may keep a record of future requests (as does the airline reservation system for flights very far in the future), future expected deliveries to stock, and other pieces of information that may aid the company in its operations.

We propose to describe in a little more detail an inventory simulation problem. The reason for simulating a situation is that we can learn about how it is apt to behave in reality without paying the cost of actually doing it. This can be of enormous value in many situations, since experimentation in real life is often not possible, while on a machine it is relatively cheap in both time and money. Thus with a good simulation we can explore many, many combinations of possible arrangements to find out the one, or the few, that meet our (apparent) needs, without paying the cost in money and possible social harm of doing the wrong ones to find out that they were wrong.

Thus we propose to explore the inventory simulation problem to find out how we should operate our inventory. We hope by simulating to avoid the cost of actually trying what will turn out to be bad strategies.

The problem, as posed first, gave the actual observed withdrawals from stock over the last 18 months and asked what would have happened had we changed our methods of stocking the supplies? In particular, what would have resulted if we had changed one or more of the following:

1. the reorder point—that is, when we placed an order for more supplies
2. the reorder amount—that is, how much we ordered at a time
3. how rapidly we got the supplies into use once they were ordered

The third item can be somewhat altered by (a) ordering by letter or telephone, and by (b) changing the delay time of the inspection group while getting the goods from the unloading dock through inspection (for acceptance) and then into the stockrooms.

The simulation of the inventory is easy in conception. We have the number of items on hand at the start of the period. We simply process the requests that had been recorded during the 18-month period, one by one, noting their dates. When necessary, we place orders and calculate the delivery date using a random process (see Chapter 8) to simulate the variability of the shipping process: add to stock when deliveries arrive, record outages of stock both in the number of requests and the length of time, and also report the amount on hand at fixed periods. The flowchart for this is left as an exercise.

As is almost always true, there were many, many complicating details. For one, the company did *not* use the normal calendar but rather the widely used sequence of 4-week, 4-week, 5-week months to form a quarter of a year—designed to make the internal comparisons of various quarterly periods more comparable. Thus there had to be a block of programming for the conversion from one calendar to the other and back at the appropriate places in the computing. Further, although we were assured that the data given were consistent, it turned out that they were not. The company records showed withdrawals from stock when there could have been nothing there, and their final totals at the end of the period did not always agree with what we computed directly from their data. We had to make up some pseudo-transactions of withdrawals and returns to have a consistent set of data.

There was also a logical flaw in the plan of research. The records that they had showed the actual withdrawals and did not include requests not filled.

Still, running the same data many times and varying the reorder times and amounts and the parameters of the random delay, we found what would likely have happened had the changes been made as requested. This helped us search for a better strategy of inventory keeping. Small improvements in inventory practice may make a great deal of difference to a company, because inventory represents capital investment not available for other purposes, taxes, storage space, deterioration of goods, possibility of loss due to theft or fire, and obsolescence. The simple simulation paid off handsomely both in economic returns and in quality of service.

This example was chosen to show how machines may be used not only to run a company from day to day, but also how they can help improve the quality of running the company by studying the underlying plans and rules the company uses.

TOTAL INFORMATION SYSTEMS   6.4

Business applications, such as payroll and inventory, generally require a lot of input and output and relatively little actual computing per item.

The cost of computing, therefore, tends to be closely bound to the cost of preparing the input and getting the information in and out of the machine.

Recognizing that the cost of operation depends greatly on the cost of getting the input information into a machine-readable form, much attention has been given by business to this aspect of computing. Besides the automatic preparation of the input by machines, there also arises the concept of a *total information system*, one in which the output of each stage serves as the input to succeeding stages. The aim of the total information system is to get the information into a machine-readable form as soon as possible, and then at every subsequent stage hold down the number of new items that humans must prepare. As a result, most of the information needed at one stage comes from the output of earlier stages.

Most Americans are customers of large organizations and already have had some experiences with the consequences of this trend. The income tax forms are precoded by a machine before they are sent. The purchase order sent in is often a form that lends itself to easy conversion to machine-readable form. Many companies either use your own writing of your name and address as the label on the package they finally send to you, or else use a machine-printed form that came from the internal company processing of your order.

Banks and other financial organizations have talked about a *cashless society*. In such a society you never need to bother with the tokens of money (coins and bills). You simply get so many units of credit from your employer and you dissipate your credit in the form of purchases, rents, investments, payments on previous loans, and so on. Each deduction is made automatically from your account and added to the other person's account. The obvious fact is that by handling all your money all the time, the banks will do better in getting a share for themselves. However, they also recognize that the next large cost savings are in avoiding the preparation of those documents that run their machines for keeping your and their records.

Business in general is moving along this same path toward a total information system: companies send prepunched forms to each other, companies file your income tax withholding on magnetic tapes with the government, and so on. The concept has the effect of gradually altering the structure of the company. Now that company executives can easily get much more data about what the company is doing, in principle they can use it to operate the company more efficiently.

But they soon find that there is more information available than they can possibly read and digest. One solution to this dilemma is to use *reporting by exception*. For example, if the expenditures are according to the budgeted plans, then only this fact is reported. It is the expenditures that are not within budget that management most needs to know about.

A second approach is to use more elaborate mathematics to make the decisions that humans used to make based on long experience and hunches. Today the company and the operation may be so vast and changing so rapidly that people cannot know what they need to know to make the decisions, nor can they learn fast enough to have reliable hunches nor build up relevant experience. In a rapidly changing situation past experience may be more of a liability than an asset. Furthermore, competition is growing so keen that there is not the latitude to make the mistakes that in the past were charged up to learning. Competition and other pressures force the use of computers, and computers in turn make it necessary to change the organization or method of doing business. All these pressures are combing to alter the traditional business practices, not only at the level that the customer sees, but at all levels in the organization. As Marshall McLuhan would say, "The tool (computers) is altering the user (business)."

MATHEMATICS IN BUSINESS 6.5

The pressure of competition, the rapidity of change, and the availability of computing machines have combined to greatly increase the use of mathematics in business. Since the Second World War several branches of mathematics have been developed that are closely connected with business problems. These supply the technical background for applications, and because they are usually unfamiliar to the average person we shall briefly look at three of the fields.

Linear programming is one of the most publicized of the new fields of mathematics that are readily applicable to some business problems. It is a mathematical method of finding the optimum solution for situations when many of the variables are constrained by simple inequalities. Often the constraint is the natural one that some quantity cannot be a negative number (since it is not possible to manufacture a negative number of items even if the formulas say that it would be optimal). Furthermore, there is often an upper limit on how much of various items the available equipment can make in a given time. It is the presence of *linear inequalities* in the statement of the problem that makes the field of linear programming different from the usual mathematical solution of linear equations. And it is the basic linearity[1] of the situation that permits the finding of the optimum with a reasonable expenditure of effort even when there are hundreds of different variables in the problem.

Game theory is another field of mathematics that has received much of the inspiration for its growth and development from economic problems. A central feature of game theory is that in many situations there may be no best strategy against an opponent who has sufficient information—there are only random mixtures of strategies. This situation is very common in games played by humans (which is where the name comes from). While the detailed working out of a game-theoretic situation is rarely done, the general philosophy of the nature of a solution has greatly influenced some areas, the military in particular. Some of this kind of thinking has been transferred to business, but so far as the author knows it has not had the same widespread influence as it has had in military thinking.

The Second World War brought forth a field called, loosely, *operations research* (often abbreviated O.R.). This might be defined as simply trying to quantify situations that were formerly thought to be only qualitative in nature. The success of operations research methods in so many aspects of the war naturally led to great hopes that it would apply to peacetime activities to a similar degree. Although the hope of the extreme optimists has not been realized, nor does it now seem likely to be in the near future, the method is often effective, and many large industrial organizations have operations research groups.

Because of the nature of the problems of operations research there is a heavy dependence on the techniques of statistics, as well as some need for game theory and linear programming, but anything that

---

[1] Linear means that (1) if cause a produces result A, then ka produces kA (where k is any constant number), and (2) if a produces A and b produces B, then $a + b$ produces $A + B$.

will help is freely used. The solution of the problems is often so complex that it is necessary to resort to computers.

These by no means exhaust the mathematical tools that are finding applications in the field of business. It is likely that in the next decade many new mathematical tools will find application in business where there is a steadily increasing pressure to do better and better or else get wiped out. Thus computers will continue to change business in the future.

AN EXAMPLE OF COMPOUND INTEREST 6.6

It is not easy to give a simple illustration using the above mathematical theories. Instead, we shall give a very simple example related to compound interest to show how a computer can aid in business operations not closely related to accounting. Of necessity the problem is almost trivial.

Money borrowed, loaned, or generally invested is usually rated by the compound interest formula

$$\text{Amount} = (1 + R)^T$$

where R is the interest rate per unit of time (usually one year) and T is the number of time intervals (correspondingly in years). The usual tables show the amount $1 will become after a given number T of time periods at a given rate R. But business managers are more likely to think in terms of the length of time it takes a given amount to double or otherwise increase by a multiplicative factor. To get this number it is necessary to scan the standard tables and interpolate in the proper place for each interest rate.

Let us pose the problem of making a table for the following: given the interest rate, how long will it take to double a given amount? Clearly the amount A is to be 2, and we are to find the time T corresponding to the rate R. But what interest rates shall we try? The common rates often run around 3 to 6 percent per year, so that surely 10 percent would be a practical top (although some lending plans have exceeded 18 percent). But the table may be used in cases where the amount is compounded quarterly, for which we use the quarterly rate

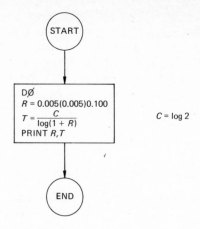

Figure 6-2

$(R/4)$ and T is now the number of quarters. Thus we might want to go as low as 1 percent or lower.

Now, how do we calculate the time T? We need to recall something about logarithms. In particular, taking the logs of both sides of the preceding equation gives

$$T = \frac{\log 2}{\log(1 + R)}$$

We will take rates from 1/2 percent, that is, $R = 0.005$, by 1/2 percent to $R = 0.100$. The flowchart is very easy to draw (Figure 6-2). Note that in this problem there seems to be no data to be read in. It might be wise to consider leaving the range to be covered in R as data so that at some later date, if further questions arise, the problem can be rerun with different input data.

While we are about it, perhaps we should think a bit more and ask questions of the form, "If I want to double my money in a given number of years, then what rate must I charge to achieve this?" Tables 6.6-1 and 2 contain the results.

Here again we have taken only the simplest example and carried the analysis out far enough so that we can see in complete detail how a machine might do the problem. The results are of only minor importance, but the effort, given an available computer, is also very minor.

Table 6.6-1   **Table 6.6-2**

Time or rate to double an amount of money.

R	T	T	R
0.005	138.98	1.0	1.000
0.010	69.66	1.1	0.878
0.015	46.56	1.2	0.782
0.020	35.00	1.3	0.704
0.025	28.07	1.4	0.641
0.030	23.45	1.5	0.587
0.035	20.15	1.6	0.542
0.040	17.67	1.7	0.503
0.045	15.75	1.8	0.470
0.050	14.21	1.9	0.440
0.055	12.95	2.0	0.414
0.060	11.90	3.0	0.260
0.065	11.01	4.0	0.189
0.070	10.24	5.0	0.149
0.075	9.58	6.0	0.122
0.080	9.01	7.0	0.104
0.085	8.50	8.0	0.091
0.090	8.04	9.0	0.080
0.095	7.64	10.0	0.072
0.100	7.27	11.0	0.065
		12.0	0.059
		13.0	0.055
		14.0	0.051
		15.0	0.047

SUMMARY   6.7

Let us recall where we have been so far in the study of computers. We have examined (Chapter 1) the general background of computing. Then we examined briefly the representation of information (Chapter 2) and the representation of processes (Chapter 3). Finally, we examined (Chapter 4) how a computing machine processes information.

We have now examined the way situations are analyzed in order to break them down into parts so that they can be organized for a computer to do (Chapters 5 and 6). Because of the restrictions on the background knowledge of the reader, we gave only simple examples. The example of the classification of triangles should have offered some idea of the mass of detail and the unstated parts of problems that tend to dominate the actual applications of computers. The business examples have not generally been carried out as far as the geometric examples were because the point had already been made. Rather, they were designed to show in somewhat broader strokes how some simple things can be done on a computer.

At this point we are going to turn to various ideas that arise in the use of computers, and the treatment will be along the lines of the main idea rather than in terms of the field of application.

In all applications there is a background of knowledge (usually technical) that is necessary for the successful application of a computer to a given situation. But more important than the technical background is the wisdom to choose which application to try and to plan the proper general approach to be adopted.

In practice, general knowledge needs to be translated into specific situations, and the specific cases that are going to be used need to be examined with great care lest we fall into the traps that await the unwary. In business applications, two aspects of vital importance are often overlooked. The first is the importance of reliability. We must not only have reliable machines, or at least adequate backup machines, but we must get the information into the machines in a reliable form. Bad data can only produce bad results. The system *as a whole* must be reliable.

Second, the system must be robust in the sense that it must be able to cope with the inevitable exceptions that occur in real life. Not only are there exceptional cases, but the system itself will evolve in time. It must therefore be robust enough to survive the changes in a reasonably healthy state of efficient, accurate operation.

By using a simulation of a situation, say, a payroll, we can often find out how a proposed system will operate *before* we put it into operation. By using our imagination and testing out various aspects of the system we can examine situations and make tests that are in practice too hard to think through for the unaided mind. Thus simulation, the topic of the next chapter, is a natural tool for use with computers.

CHAPTER 7

Leibniz Calculator (Gottfried Leibniz, 1646-1716)
From a replica in the IBM Corporation Antique Calculator Collection.

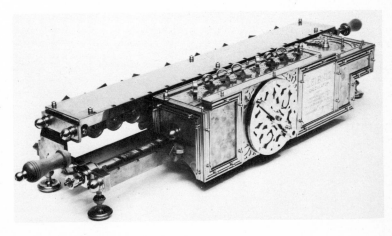

7

Models and Simulation

By *model*, we do not mean a girl modeling clothes. We mean a copy of some aspects of the original. An exact copy is hardly a model—it is the real thing. So, necessarily, some degree of abstraction or idealization is implied by the word *model*, and some aspects of the original are omitted.

Consider the simple model of counting students registering for a course by tallying a mark for each student on a piece of paper. In this model each registrant is represented by a single mark. Simple as this model is (*simple* meaning we are omitting many aspects of the person when we use a single line to mean one person), it has the remarkable property of enabling us to predict some things quite accurately. Thus if we want to know the total number of students in the class, we can operate on the model and count the number of marks on the piece of paper. If we want to know the total number of students in all the history courses, we can add up all the marks in the individual history courses. It is remarkable that so simple a model should agree with what would be found if you counted all the individual history students.[1] We are so accustomed to this type of model that we take its many predictive properties for granted.

This model shows both the strength and the weakness of making models. It has many predictive properties, but it also has many limitations. If we tried to use the color of the marks on the piece of paper (say, some were by chance in red pencil, some in blue, some in black, some in ink, and so on) to predict the color of the eyes of the students, we would almost certainly fail. The model makes no attempt to cover such aspects. But for its domain of application the model is clearly much easier to manipulate and use than is reality, that is, the groups of students.

Philosophers have long argued that we can never know reality. All we can think about are mental images (models) of reality. They base this belief, in part, on the fact that our senses only report to us *part* of reality, never reality in total. In their view *we* are talking about models of models, but it is usually not worth the effort to make this distinction, and we shall therefore speak "carelessly" of modeling reality.

To some extent the words *model* and *simulation* are used interchangeably. If there is a difference, then it is that models tend to center around building the static part and simulation around the working out of the dynamic part of the situation. One might make the distinction that we model a situation and simulate a process. Thus we speak of a model of a neuron and the simulation of a space shot. We will make no clear distinction between these two words but will tend to conform to common usage, which appears to make some small distinction along the lines indicated.

Models and Simulations Already Discussed

The airline reservation system we briefly mentioned is a model or simulation. Selected storage registers in the computer represent (correspond to, or *model*) seats in a plane on a given flight on a given day. The placing of names for reservations and the canceling of reservations simulate the corresponding processes.

The inventory simulation we examined is another example of

---

[1] A student registered in two different history courses is being counted as two history students. This simple model does not allow us to study this type of duplication.

modeling. This time a number in a storage register corresponds to (models) the number of items of a given type that are in the stock room, and the computing simulated the actual inventory changes that would have occurred.

It is a bit more difficult to view the computation of the regular polygons and the circumscribed circles as a simulation, but with some effort it can be done. Indeed, one view of computers is that they are simply big, expensive, flexible devices for manipulating models. Without taking this extreme view we claim that a lot of computing can be conveniently viewed as modeling or simulation, and that, as would be expected, manipulating the model by the machine is very often much cheaper, and more flexible, than is manipulating the real thing. And often for practical reasons, the real thing either cannot be manipulated, or else it is not socially desirable to experiment on the real thing.

THE VALIDITY OF A MODEL   7.2

The question arises continually as to the *validity of a model*—usually phrased in terms of the *truth*, *reliability*, or *correctness* of the model. Let us state at once that there can be no proof that the model is exactly correct for all cases. We simply cannot get a guaranteed correspondence between the material world and the symbolic world. Furthermore, we have by definition ignored or idealized certain aspects of reality. There-fore we cannot expect identical behavior in all aspects.

We can get reasonable degrees of confidence for certain types of questions based, in part, on past experience. Perhaps the best verified, elaborate model is classical Newtonian mechanics. It was found to predict very accurately the positions of the planets, and it has even predicted where to point a telescope to find new planets. Nevertheless, Newtonian mechanics was ultimately found not to apply in situations where the velocities are comparable to the velocity of light. When the velocity is high it is necessary to use the model of *relativity*. Again, where very small sizes are concerned, the model of *quantum mechanics* more accurately predicts what will be observed than does Newtonian mechanics.

Of all the models humans have created for dealing with various situations, the abstract model called *probability theory* is perhaps the most fascinating. Probability does not claim that a specific coin, die, or roulette wheel will behave in a certain fashion. Rather, what we observe is that, on the average, specific realizations of the model agree surprisingly well with the predictions of probability theory. When there is disagreement between observation and model, it is *always assumed* not that the probability model is wrong but rather that our specific application to reality is wrong! It seems to be impossible to think of an experimental outcome that would overthrow the general model (theory) of probability. Exceptions are always blamed on reality: the coin was not well balanced, it was not tossed properly, and so on.

Thus models occupy a peculiar position. Some can be overthrown completely or partially by observation, and some apparently cannot—they appear to be founded on logic rather than experience. Models are tools of the mind, and some are so basic to our ways of thinking that we usually prefer to deny reality than to give up our habits of thought.

Some models also appear to contradict other models in the sense that for different purposes we use different models of the same thing. For example, in talking about a table top we are apt to regard it as solid and continuous if we are concerned with elasticity and strength, but we regard it as mostly empty space with a few electrons and nuclei here and there if we are looking at it in fine detail, as we do in nuclear physics. The models are not contradictory; they are used for different purposes.

As another example of the use of different models, consider the question of free will. If you are acting as a psychologist you assume that "the person being what he is and the situation being what it is the person can only do as he does." Without this tacit assumption there is not apt to be a theory of psychology. But when talking and arguing with a friend you are apt to assume that he has free will and can do and say as he pleases. The models do not contradict each other so much as they supplement each other. Each has its uses, and to get them mixed up is about as foolish as to get the continuous and atomic models of the table top mixed up. And it is probably as foolish to argue which is the more true, for how would you decide? What test would you accept as conclusive?

The validity of a model arises, then, from at least two sources. One is logical appeal, and the other is past experience with the model. In setting up a new model, therefore, it is necessary to consider how you are going to develop enough confidence so that it can be used in new situations. Some models, like the counting of the students, have both a past experience factor and a basic logical appeal that are so overwhelming as to require no new verification. But many models are not so favored and require thought and experience to produce confidence. The appropriateness of the model for the kind of questions to be asked is also an essential consideration. When, as in Newtonian mechanics, the kind of question asked is changed, or the range of the variables is extended, then the model may no longer predict as well as it did before, and new models such as relativity and quantum mechanics need to be considered.

THE DEGREE OF MODELING 7.3

At first thought it would appear that a situation should be modeled as completely as possible. But the simple example of counting students shows that for its purposes the replacement of the very complex object, the human, by a simple mark on a piece of paper is all that is necessary. To also record a number of other features of the human, such as height, weight, color of hair, would be a waste of time and would probably confuse the record keeping.

In the inventory simulation we used a random number to determine the delivery date of the order for new supplies. Thus we simulated (modeled) the variations in the delivery system. Was it necessary to do so? Would not the use of the average delay have given about the same results?

There are various answers to these questions. If the variability in delivery time is large, then probably the effect would be noticeable. But if the variability is small, then it would probably not be noticeable. To be safe, people tend to include everything that might possibly affect the result, but this is costly in many ways. To include a lot of detail is to

1. incur more preparation time, both in finding out the facts to be modeled and in programming the machine
2. increase the computer time used, often markedly
3. obscure the effects that are being examined

(In the inventory simulation an observed variation *might* have been due to an unfortunate sequence of late deliveries rather than be the effect of the parameter that was changed.)

There is a strong tendency, especially for managers, to ask for complete modeling of all aspects, but it is probably best to model as little as will still capture the essence of the object being modeled. Later, with increased understanding of how the model works, you can gradually make it more elaborate. The amount that is necessary to model to capture the essence of the situation being modeled is, of course, a matter of judgment. Clarity of thought and experience are the main guides. Critics of the results will always cite how much was left out and maintain that things would be different if you had included them. But, let us repeat, *experience* seems to indicate that overdetailing the model is more often the mistake than is underdetailing. It may not be easy to add detail, however, unless it is carefully planned for.

STABLE AND UNSTABLE MODELS   7.4

Suppose we wished to model a junction transistor. One approach would be to divide the region under consideration into a large number of small subregions and to set up the equations which interrelate the various subregions. We would then impose the external forces and compute, following the given laws of behavior obtained from technical knowledge of the field (solid state physics), how each region would behave in the next short interval of time. Then we would advance the time one unit, and again compute how each region would behave now that it is subjected to the new forces from the slightly changed adjacent regions. During each time interval we would calculate how each subregion would change. The many, many repetitions of the same pattern of computation over each subregion and then over each interval of time would finally give us the behavior of the entire system.

In this fashion, using the equations appropriate to each subinterval, we can calculate the complex behavior of the whole transistor. In a sense this is often the secret of the power of the large-scale digital computer. Many, many repetitions of the same pattern of computation applied to varying data produces the complex result for the entire system.

An apparently similar problem, the prediction of weather, would proceed in somewhat the same way. We would divide up the atmosphere into appropriate blocks, and write the appropriate equations describing the changes that would occur in each block if it were subjected to the external forces from adjacent blocks in terms of given physical variables like temperature, density, humidity, etc. Then in the same way as in the case of the transistor, given the initial measurements of the atmosphere, we would compute how the whole system would evolve in time. But there is a significant difference between the two models. Usually for the transistor, small changes in the initial conditions, or in the parameters of the material, produce small differences in the final result. In the weather model, however, small differences in the initial conditions ultimately produce enormous differences in predicted weather.

The transistor problem is said to be *stable* in the sense that small changes in either the input or in the computing produce only small changes in the output. The weather problem is said to be *unstable* in that small changes lead to arbitrarily large changes later on. Note that the difference does not lie in the way we used the computer, but rather in the nature of the problem itself.

It should be evident that we cannot expect to calculate precisely the unstable weather problem very far into the future because we cannot expect to know the initial conditions sufficiently accurately. There are, however, stabilizing effects that do give some encouragement in the matter. The sun shines steadily, seasons do follow seasons, and in some fashion small changes are erased in the flow of the seasons. Thus there are some hopes for long-range forecasts.

Perhaps the ultimate in unstable problems is the prediction of human behavior in detail. Consider a situation in which you are hurrying to catch a plane. In running around a corner you bump into a lady and practically knock her down. You pause to help her get rearranged and pick up the loose ends, and then a year later you marry her. One second sooner or one second later and you would not have met her at all! All of us have had many experiences in which very small differences at one time in our lives have apparently produced very large differences later on.

On the other hand, insurance companies predict quite successfully the *average* human behavior with regard to death and illnesses. Some average human behaviors are possible to predict, especially with the aid of machines to follow out the complex model, but detailed behavior of the human individual seems to be beyond hope because of the inherent complexity as well as the difficulty of making the necessary measurements. But, like the weather, one can predict that the "ages of man" will follow their accustomed cycle, and an examination of the aging of selected ancestors may give clues to the rapidity of the coming of the various ages for a specific individual. Again, one must be careful to understand what can and cannot be modeled successfully. Average behavior, typical behavior, and gross behavior of humans may be predicted if the appropriate models are created, but it appears that detailed specific models of individual complex behavior cannot be produced for practical computer solutions.

LEVELS OF SIMULATIONS   7.5

Let us return to the common problem of business modeling. At the simplest level are the payroll, inventory, purchases, and sales orders—in general, the classical domain of bookkeeping and accounting practice.

At the next level is the simulation of the production lines and the problem of scheduling the equipment of production and transportation facilities. These problems have given rise to new mathematical theories in recent years. At about the same level, we have the problems of marketing and advertising.

Above this level is the matter of simulating the consequences of corporate policy. This is sometimes called *industrial dynamics* and is only gradually being developed. The simulation of the inventory is a trivial example of simulating policy. It is used for answering questions like, "If we adopt the following policies for reordering times and amounts and assume the speeds of delivery, what will be the consequences to the company?"

But the larger interrelations between the various policy decisions are, as we said, only gradually coming under study. Consider a policy that decides that when there is a large backlog of orders the inventory should be built up to meet demands. (It would appear to be safe to do so because of the increasing demand for the goods.) This decision leads to the hiring of more workers to fill *both* the increased needs to meet sales and for the inventory storage. When the demand on the goods levels off, it brings the decision to reduce inventory, thus laying off workers to decrease production. This ultimately produces a new demand for goods since the lower production rate is not adequate to meet normal demand. Thus, in some instances at least, the policy itself may create a cycle in the volume of production that is not present in the actual demand for the goods. Evidently it is important to study the way corporate policies will be interrelated, and the computing machine provides a powerful tool for exploring such models.

It is also true that the managers are beginning to ask, "If we try this new policy, what will happen to the company?" To answer such questions it is necessary to have reliable models of both the inside and the outside of the company. Of course, the models must be idealizations of the entire economy, and it is still an art to select those parts that seem to be essential and relevant and to ignore those which can probably be safely neglected.

The point is that models of the business situation can be formulated, and the models can give the managers some ideas of "what might happen if . . . ." They can also reveal the causes of past troubles *provided* enough records of the past were kept. How does the machine do the simulation? Simply. Given the descriptions of the various processes and their interrelationships—that is, a model—and given the appropriate data (information), the computing machine carries out the simulation, often surprisingly crudely, that the model requires it to do, and then the results of the simulation are identified with the appropriate variables in the real world.

Often the model permits computing things that cannot be done in reality, or at least might be so expensive as to forbid their trial. In a recent case that came to the attention of the author, a company was interested in making a change in their sales policy. It was estimated that it would take at least 6 months before the effect of the change could be determined, and if the change were bad then, at least another 6 months to undo, if ever, the change and its effects. Thus there was great wariness about making the change and a general reluctance to try it at all. Had there been a reasonably reliable model of the customer and his reactions, then the change could have been simulated to see what would likely happen. But we are only in the beginnings of the development of adequate models of the consuming public since reliable data and facts are extremely hard to come by. In the absence of reliable models many large companies make special field trials of proposed new items or of various ways of advertising, trying to find out at a moderate cost what would happen if they tried it on a larger scale.

Let us summarize by again noting that the machine merely processes the model according to instructions. It is the human who (1) formulates the model, (2) organizes the information (the sequence of 0s and 1s that represents the information, Chapter 2), (3) writes the relationships and transformations used in the processes (Chapter 3), and (4) decides the relevance of the results. The machine (Chapter 4) is only the tool that is used to carry out the multitudinous details of the simulation.

TRAFFIC SIMULATION   7.6

The problem in presenting to the reader what computers can do is not that of finding some application of computers, but rather to find ones that the average person knows enough about so that the material seems intelligible. One common experience is automobile traffic. Suppose we try to simulate traffic. We will need a lot of different kinds of data. For example, we will have to get, probably from direct observation, the typical distance between cars in traffic as a function of speed and kind of highway. And we will need other variables, too, such as time of day, season, density of traffic, etc. We will not only have to find the average distances but also some measures of the variability from driver to driver.

We then will be in a position to simulate the effect of one person's suddenly slowing down. Typically it will be found that under some conditions a shock wave will propagate backwards, almost at the velocity of the moving traffic, and that as you go "downstream" the slowing down will become more and more marked until the cars are actually stopping. Most observant motorists have seen these shock waves at one time or another going down the opposite lane of traffic. The source may merely be one man cutting in front of another and forcing the second man to slow down briefly. The consequence may be many drivers far behind him coming to a full stop!

When we can successfully simulate some of the observed phenomena we gain some confidence in our model, and we can begin to experiment to see if we can find new effects. One example that has been demonstrated is that if at the entrance to a tunnel the cars are artificially bunched with gaps between them, then the small variations that give rise to the shock wave effect are broken up by the gaps before the wave can get completely developed. As a consequence the total carrying capacity of the tunnel may be greater when the traffic is artificially bunched than when it is left to each driver to pick his own spacing. Actual field experiments have confirmed this effect.

Some Details of the Traffic Model

In general, we have been talking about computers and solving problems on them at the level of large blocks in the flowchart (Chapter 3). To bring them down to detailed block or flowcharts would usually require years of effort. The simple traffic problem was introduced partially to let us repeat once more the process of carrying a flowchart a bit further.

For this example we shall consider the case of uniformly moving traffic with uniformly spaced cars, and put in a slight slowing down of the first car.

Thus we assign, say, 20 (we may have to increase it to 50 later) registers for the positions of 20 consecutive cars, and another set for storing their velocities. Let us express the position in feet, and velocity in feet per second. We might, for example, use a 100-foot spacing as appropriate for a 50-feet-per-second velocity (30 mph is 44 feet per second).

In one time interval (one second) we will advance each car by

velocity × time = 50 feet

Running several intervals to convince ourselves that all is well, we now suddenly decrease the velocity of the first car to 40 feet per second.

At the end of another second the next car sees the car ahead is only 90 feet away and he adjusts his velocity (somewhat late, as it is in reality) by the formula that gives his attempted velocity as a function of the distance and velocity of the car in front of him. Evidently this function, which we have not given explicitly, must have the property that, when spacing is 100 feet, velocity is 50 feet per second.

Now we calculate the positions of all the cars at the end of the next second, then the next, etc., and we have the simulation (provided we remember to print out the results).

We have omitted the formula for the velocity sought when an observed distance and velocity of the car in front is seen (late). As this formula is changed we will get different effects. Thus the crux of the simulation lies in this formula.

Do we have enough information to make up such a formula if all we have is speculation? (We could go out and measure traffic or consult traffic books for what typically happens, but we will persist in the armchair approach.) We know that the stopping distance of a car is roughly proportional to the square of the velocity, so higher speeds (because of the reaction time) tend to produce greater spacings.

Thus, by a simple program, first making reasonable assumptions of the spacing that motorists try to maintain as a function of the speed they are going, and then causing one car of the moving stream of equally spaced cars going at a constant speed to slow down (on the computer we decrease the rate of growth of the number representing the position of the car), and, finally, simply tracking the subsequent positions of the following cars, we can demonstrate this effect. Under some assumptions the shock wave effect can be clearly seen. Thus the computer provides a laboratory tool for traffic study by simulating the real world with a simple model. Now that the effect has been shown to arise with equally spaced cars, it is easy to elaborate the model to consider variable spacing and variable driving characteristics and examine these more realistic models.

EXERCISE—7.6
Try several of your own formulas on five cars for five cycles and find (by hand) a formula that apparently shows the shock effect.

THREE-DIMENSIONAL TIC-TAC-TOE   7.7

The widely played game of three-dimensional tic-tac-toe provides a simple example of how a simulation can be programmed for a computer. The game board consists of four layers, each having a four-by-four set of places where a piece (man) can be placed. In total there are 64 places where a man can be placed. (Figures 7-1 and 7-4) The game is played by two people, you and your opponent, alternately placing a man in some unoccupied place on the board. The object of the game is to get four of your men on a straight line before your opponent gets four of his men on a line. The game is difficult because there are 76 different straight lines to be considered.

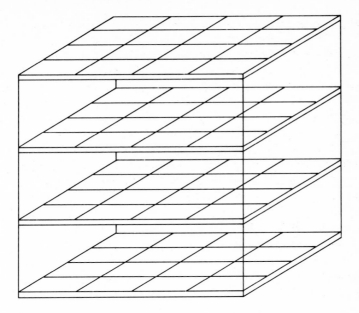

Figure 7-1

At this point we propose to analyze only the simplest elements of a strategy of play and leave further elaboration to Chapter 14. Let us suppose that your opponent has just announced his move and that it is your turn to play. First you must check to find out if his move is legal—that he has not moved where there is already a man.

If it is a legal move then the next thing to do is look to see if you have three men on a line on which the fourth position is blank. If you find such a line, then the obvious move evidently produces an immediate win for you.

If there is no such winning move for you, then you should next search to see if *he* already has three on a line with the fourth position open. If he has, you should move there to block him, or else he will win on the next move.

If neither side has three on a line, then search for lines which have two of your men and two blanks. If any pair of such lines have a point in common, and if the common point is blank, then this position is called a *fork*. The importance of a fork is that if you play your man on

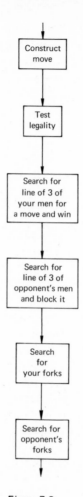

Figure 7-2

the point common to the two lines this will produce two lines each with three of your men. The opponent cannot block both on his next move. Therefore, on your next move you can win. (See Figure 7-3.)

If you have no forks, evidently it is worth looking to see if he has any. It does not follow that you must *immediately* block his potential fork (or forks). You could also take a line with two of your men on it and add a third. This forces him to play on the fourth position on that

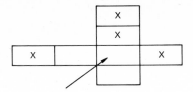

Figure 7-3

line to prevent your win on your next move (which would occur before he could cash in on his fork). By a sequence of such *forcing moves* it might be possible to break up his fork (or forks). At this point we shall only consider finding the fork.

Some Details of Programing Tic-Tac-Toe

We now come to the problem of representing the information describing the board position (Chapter 2). We number the positions on the board from 1 to 64 in any convenient manner (Figure 7-4). We will assume that the word length of the computer we are using is at least 64 bits. (If it is shorter we could use two or more words as if they were one word, and only the details of what follows would be different.) This means that corresponding to each position on the board there is a position of a bit in the word. We can put 1s in a word in all the positions where your men are, and 1s in a second word in the positions where the opponent's men are. These two words, then, will completely describe the board position at any stage of the game.

The analysis we gave of a strategy for playing the game was mainly in terms of lines. An examination of the game shows that there are 76 possible lines on the 4 X 4 X 4 board. We shall represent each line by a word which has a 1 in each bit position corresponding to a board position that is on the line, and a 0 in all the other positions. Thus each line is described by a word having four 1s and the rest 0s.

13	14	15	16
9	10	11	12
5	6	7	8
1	2	3	4

29	30	31	32
25	26	27	28
21	22	23	24
17	18	19	20

45	46	47	48
41	42	43	44
37	38	39	40
33	34	35	36

61	62	63	64
57	58	59	60
53	54	55	56
49	50	51	52

Figure 7-4

For instance, the line through positions 1, 5, 9, 13 is represented by a word with 1 bits in positions 1, 5, 9, 13, and zeros elsewhere.

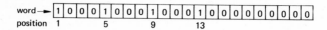

Another example is the line through 5, 22, 39, 56 whose word has 1s in those positions.

For each line we will want certain extra information, so with each word describing a line we shall associate a second word which tells us

1. if the line is "dead"—a dead line has at least one of your men and at least one of your opponent's men, and so can never be used to win.
2. if the line is blank (unoccupied by any men)
3. if you or your opponent controls the line (if it is alive)
4. how many men are on the line, if it is alive (see Figure 7-5)

Let us assign the first bit of the associated word for each line so that a 1 means that the line is dead and a 0 that it is alive. We assign the second bit so that a 0 means the line is blank and a 1 means that it is occupied. The third bit is a 0 if your men are on the line and a 1 if the opponent's men are on the line. Finally, we assign a pair of bits to give the number of men there are on the line (2 bits because there can be up to three men). These assignments are not completely arbitrary. We have been looking ahead a little to see how the program will be written in more detail.

The first step in the expansion of the initial plan toward a

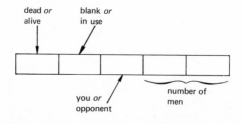

Figure 7-5

program that will actually run on a machine is to take the given move and create a word that has a 1 in the position of the move and a 0 in all other positions. This makes the information about the move available for manipulation by the machine.

To test the legality of the opponent's move we can use the AND instruction (see Section 4.2). The AND operation records a 1 in a position only if *both* words being combined have a 1 in that position. Otherwise, the AND instruction records a 0 in that position. If we AND the word describing the move with the word describing the opponent's board position, a 1 will appear only if he already had a man there, and this indicates an illegal move. Testing the result of the AND for all 0s will reveal this. Similarly, combining the word describing the move with your board position word, we check that he is not moving where you already have a man. If both tests are all 0s then we ØR the word (see Section 4.2), describing the move with his board position, thus up-dating the board position. The ØR operation puts a 1 in a position if either of the words has a 1 in that position, and a 0 if both have 0s there.

We must now update the information about the lines so that it corresponds to the new board position. To do this, we must find all the lines that the move affects. We again take the word with the single 1 describing the opponent's move, AND it with each line in turn, and then test each result for all 0s. If it is all 0s, that means the move is not on that line and the line can be ignored. The word describing the line acts like a *mask* through which we look at the move (See Figure 7-6). We see the move through the mask only if the move is at a position on the line. When we find a line that is affected by the move, we first

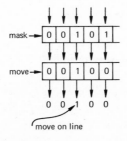

Figure 7-6

decide if the line is dead by examining the first bit of the associated word. If the line is dead we do nothing, but if it is alive we examine the second bit to see if it is occupied. If it is not occupied, then we change the "occupied bit" to a 1, set the next bit so that it indicates that the opponent occupies the line, and add 1 to the number of men on the line.

We need to return to the point where we might have found the line occupied. If it was occupied, then we need to see if it was occupied by you or by your opponent. If it was your line, then his move killed the line and we need to change the first bit accordingly. (Set it to 1, indicating a dead line.) If he occupied the line, then we add 1 to the number of men on the line.

This process must be repeated for each line on the list. When this is done we have updated our records completely, and we are ready to follow out our strategy.

Under the assumption that the opponent just moved, it is now your turn. The first step is to examine the lines to find a live line which belongs to you (item 3) and which also has three men on the line. The details of this search are easy to construct. If you find such a line, then you need to find out where the blank position is. This can be done by the AND operation of that line with your board position: three 1s will appear in positions corresponding to the positions of your men on the line. LOGICAL ADD (see Section 4.2) of the line mask with the immediately previous result (containing three 1s) will convert those 1s to 0s, while a 1 will appear in the position you should move to (see Figure 7-7).

If you come to the end of the list of lines, then you have not found such a move. Next, you essentially repeat the same search to find out if the opponent has three on a line. If he does, you construct your move in the same way to block his immediate win.

If you still have not found a move to make, then you need to search for forks. To find them you can start searching down the list of lines, looking for a live line with two of your men on it. Keeping this line and its location in the list, continue the search for live lines with two of your men. Having found a second such line (if any), how can you find if there is a common unoccupied position? If you AND the masks of the two lines you will find a 1 in the common position *if* there is one. If there is a common position, ANDing this with your board position will show all 0s if it is free for you to play there. A 1 shows

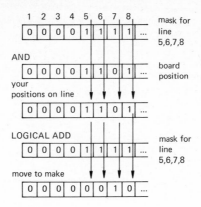

Figure 7-7

that you already have a man there. If it is free, the AND result of the two lines indicates the move to make.

If there is no fork using the first line found that has two of your men on it, then the search is resumed down the list until you find a second live line with two of your men. Again, keep this line and its location in the list and compare it with every live line below it in the list that has two of your men to see if the two lines have a common position. Repeating this process, we either find a fork or else we come out at the bottom of the list and we must go to the next stage of the strategy.

It is evident that the search for the opponent's forks is done almost the same way, but as we observed, it is not clear that you want to immediately block such forks. It may be that a sequence of *forcing moves* on your part can bring about a winning position for you, and you would be foolish to let the opponent get the initiative.

The purpose of this example is to show once more how the elementary operations of a computer can be combined to produce larger patterns and accomplish larger goals. In this example we have an illustration of the fact that computers can do much more than simple arithmetic. The problem is much more an exercise in logic than in arithmetic. We have also shown how the form of the information can affect the way the processes of the problem are written. We have carefully chosen a representation of the board position and line structure that makes the programming of the part we developed very simple. We do not contend that this is the simplest or the best way to program the problem. For instance, it should be evident that once a line is dead it should be removed somehow from the list and never examined again.

EXERCISES—7.7

1. Draw a flowchart of the strategy as described in the text and discuss how to use the same blocks of coding for both players' positions.

2. If we had represented the board positions by two lists, those of your men and those of the opponents, discuss how you would program the strategy.

3. Show how the number of 76 lines is arrived at.

4. Describe the positions on the board that have seven lines through them and those that have only four lines. Are these points more relevant in some sense than points on fewer lines? Devise a strategy that takes this into account.

LIST PROCESSING   7.7

In the previous section, lines that became dead were of no further interest, but we continually had to examine them to reaffirm that they were dead. It would have been more convenient to remove them from the list of lines, but that would have left a gap in the list, unless we moved up every entry in the list that was below the dead one. If the list is at all long, closing up the gaps can be very expensive of machine time.

Frequently we want to make what amounts to random additions or removals from a list of items, and we do not want to move all the entries below the one we are changing every time a change is made. The technical idea of a *list* was invented to handle this kind of situation economically. A list is a sequence of items of information, each followed by the address of the next entry in the list.

As an example, suppose we had items of information A,B,C,D,E, F,G, and we wanted them in the sequence

ADEFBGC

using addresses beginning at 1066. Table 7.8-1 shows how this can be done.

The words can be located anywhere, so long as each one contains the address of the next. There is no necessity for any particular order in actual storage.

Suppose we want to insert item H (which is in 1075) between E

storage address	items	next address
1066	START	1067
1067	A	1070
1068	B	1073
1069	C	1074
1070	D	1071
1071	E	1072
1072	F	1068
1073	G	1069
1074	END	
1075	H	

and F. To do this we only have to change the address that occurs with E to 1075 and put the old address that was with E, namely, 1072, with H.

Similarily, if we wished to delete item C, we change the address in its predecessor, which is G, from 1069 to 1074.

If the word length of the computer cannot hold both the information and the address of the next item in the list, then with each word in our list we can associate another word (or words). For example, associated with the information at 1066 we could use that in 1166, with 1067 associate 1167, and so on.

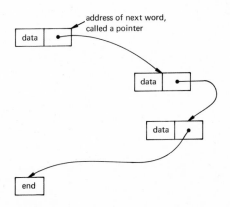

Figure 7-8

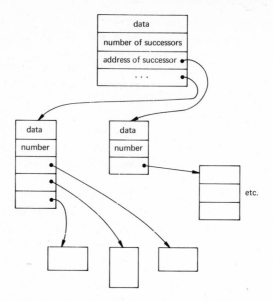

Figure 7-9

This technique of handling lists of items when additions, deletions, and rearrangements are frequent is widely used.

The list structure can be considerably more complex than the simple chain described above. For example, we might have a situation where an element in the list can have several successors instead of just one. We can draw such a list schematically as in Figure 7-9. This branching type of list is often called a tree, for obvious reasons.

It might be desirable to have pointers or links in both directions rather than in just one, as in Figure 7-10.

List processing is the term used for manipulations involving these

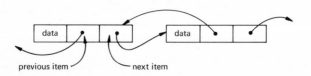

Figure 7-10

flexible data structures. Special computer programming languages have been written to make it easy for the programmer to express list operations.

List processing and list-processing languages were first developed in the late 1950s for handling complicated arrangements of data that arose in artificial intelligence applications (see Chapter 14), and they have gradually come into wider and wider use.

SUMMARY 7.9

We have introduced the idea of a model (or simulation, if it is a process) and have shown some of the necessary limitations of modeling. The computer is merely a tool to carry out the details of the modeling. It should be clear that models are what the computer handles, not reality, even when the computer interacts directly with the material world. The program that the computer follows is always based upon a model.

Modern science currently emphasizes the fact that even scientific theories are models—model is the "in word" these days in many fields. From the practical point of view, the important models are stable ones.

Much of the importance of the computer in modern society can be best understood when the computer is viewed as a device to carry out the art of modeling of complex situations. The art of constructing the basic model is very important and is often the crux of the whole problem, but little can be said in detail—beyond the obvious. The ability to carry out a simulation is an important process to master.

Finally, we have again given some of the details necessary to put a problem on a computer, and we introduced the important idea of a list of items.

CHAPTER 8

Babbage Difference Engine (Charles Babbage, 1791-1871)
From a replica in the IBM Corporation Antique Calculator Collection.

8

Randomness, Probability, and Statistics

THE IDEA OF RANDOMNESS 8.1

The use of computers in many particular situations requires, as we have repeatedly remarked, both special knowledge in the field of application and general knowledge in the field of mathematics. Of all the branches of mathematics, probability is one of the most used. Unfortunately, the probability that the average person learns in school (if any at all) is very formal and does not touch on the underlying bases of probability theory and statistics. It is necessary to understand the nature of probability and statistics if we are to later explain many of the applications that occur when using computers. This is why it is necessary to devote a chapter to what appears to be a part of formal mathematics, but which in fact is actually more philosophy than mathematics.

Randomness has usually been viewed as something to be avoided if possible. It is only recently that we have begun to use randomness in a creative fashion, especially in conjunction with computing machines. It is therefore necessary to examine what we mean by a *random* event, and the kinds of *probability* that are actually used.

Random means unpredictable, but does not imply *equally likely*. This is often a source of confusion and should be kept clearly in mind.

Figure 8-1

EXPERIMENTAL PROBABILITY   8.2

If we take a thumb tack and toss it in the air it will come to rest on a smooth, hard, level surface in one of two positions, either with the point directly up or with the tack on its side and the point touching the surface (Figure 8-1). (We are ignoring the conceptual possibility of the tack resting on its point.) Which way it comes up is a *random event*, that is, what will happen is not predictable.

Closely connected with randomness is the idea of *probability*. There are essentially three different approaches to probability. The frequency (experimental) approach estimates the probability of an event (say, the point of the thumb tack directly up) as the frequency with which it is observed to happen. Thus if we toss the thumb tack 1000 times and observe that 325 times the point is up in the air, then we say that the probability that a toss will end up with the point being up in the air is approximately 325/1000 = .325, and the probability of the opposite is 675/1000 = .675. In the frequency approach we do not say that the probability is exactly something, but the more we toss the tack the more confidence we place in the estimated probability (though this does not mean that we are always more nearly correct!)

We believe that if we were to toss the tack another 100 times then we would observe around 32 or 33 times with the point up, and we would be surprised if the observed number were as far from this prediction as, say, 10. We recognize that by chance we might see a full 100 points up, but we feel that, from the earlier experience of the 1000 tosses, this is extremely unlikely.

This, then, is the essence of the frequency approach: a number of trials are made and the number of successes divided by the total number of trials gives us an estimate of the probability of the event happening. From this observed probability we make predictions on what we are likely to see if further trials are made. But we have no certainly that the first sequence of trials was a "good sample," nor that in the future we will not occasionally get very different answers. What we do is about all that can be done in such situations.

LOGICAL PROBABILITY 8.3

The second approach is from reasoning (often called a priori reasoning). Given a "well-balanced coin," we expect that about half of the time when we toss the coin we will get heads and half the time we will get tails. In this case we *assign* the exact probability of 1/2 to each of heads and tails. If in a long run of tosses we do not observe this ratio of successes to total tosses, we are apt to say that "the coin is not well-balanced," that "we are not tossing it randomly," or that "it is an unlikely run of events."

Similarly, for a die with six sides, we usually assign the exact probability 1/6 to any given side of the die facing up. The assignment of 1/6 is done by pure reason and not by observed measurement. Most cases of logical probability are based on "geometric probability." We believe that with a symmetric situation, there is no reason for events not being equally likely. But this field is full of pitfalls for the unwary!

In principle, there is no way of connecting the two models together—in practice they work together very well. We do observe the frequencies predicted by the reasoning from symmetric coins, dice, roulette wheels, etc., when we try long runs. We also find that the frequency approach gives probabilities that can be used quite as successfully as if they were pure reason probabilities. In the thumb tack case it would be hard to deduce from measurements of the tack itself, and the way it was tossed, what the probabilities should be unless we make a sequence of trials, although theoretically it might be possible.

SUBJECTIVE (PERSONAL) PROBABILITY 8.4

In addition to the two types of probability we have just discussed, the frequency and the logical, there has recently been a development of a third kind, often called *subjective probability*. This topic is in a great state of flux, full of argument, discussion, and little agreement among the main contenders.

We shall approach the topic by giving a brief history of its growth (as it appears to the author). The Second World War brought to prominence a number of methods related to operations research. Among the questions that bothered people was the meaning of a sentence like "The soldier has a 90 percent probability of being killed in this encounter." When a general said this, the confusion could be smoothed over by pretending it meant something like, "In the general's experience, he felt that about 9 out of 10 soldiers were killed in very similar events." But what could it possibly mean to the individual soldier? He has only one life, and the frequency approach is meaningless to him.

Similarly, in everyday life we face situations in which there is really no frequency of repetition. For instance, we use a probability such as "taking a chance" in running across the street in heavy traffic, or explicitly mention probability, as in "so and so has a 60 percent chance of winning the election if he runs," or "the patient has a 30 percent probability of survival." The question of the meaning that should be associated with such statements can no longer be ignored.

The classical approach to probability is to imagine the one sample that you have as being embedded in an *ensemble* of similar events. We imagine an ensemble of similar events and regard what we see as a sample drawn at random from the ensemble. This approach is unconvincing to the postwar scientists. To take one of the author's experiences as an example, I was once shown some data gathered on the number of English poets who were alive during each year for several hundred years. Passing over the question of how the data was obtained, the question being asked of me was, "How real is the impressive cycle of about 50 years that a plot of the data seems to indicate?" I took the question to a leading statistician who was then following the accepted doctrine of the day and he advised embedding it in a suitable ensemble of similar cases. I said, "If you mean that I am to gather similar data on Irish poets, French poets, and so on, to form the ensemble, you are crazy because there simply isn't enough time nor is it practical to spend all that effort." Further and wilder suggestions for forming the needed ensemble brought forth the admission that the proposed ensemble that I was to imagine either would not affect the final conclusion (in which case why bother?) or else it would affect the conclusion (and since I would be merely guessing at the ensemble, that would be equally unsatisfactory). The whole approach was of theoretical interest only.

Attempts to apply statistics to these new situations gradually rehabilitated the old Bayesian probability (a technical point in classical probability theory) and brought forth studies of what we mean when we make subjective probability judgments. The results of such studies so far are not in complete agreement.

We shall later need to discuss how these three kinds of probability are used in computer applications.

PROBABILITY DISTRIBUTION 8.5

Given a random trial with a number of different outcomes there is a distribution of probabilities of the possible outcomes. Thus the trial "take a word at random from a book and measure the number of letters it contains" leads to a frequency distribution such as was given in Chapter 2. The probability distribution would be obtained if we divided the number of times a particular outcome happened by the total number of trials (in this example we are using 250). Curiously enough, to get 250 random words we selected 250 *consecutive* words! (The attempt to find 250 random, isolated, words is more difficult than it at first appears. For instance, randomly opening to a page and stabbing to find a random word would favor longer words!)

If we tried tossing a die we would expect to see a probability distribution of 1/6 for each of the six possible outcomes. Tossing a coin should give a probability distribution of 1/2 for each of the two possible cases, heads or tails.

Some distributions are not discrete, but are continuous. Thus if we break a twig of length 6 inches at a random place, all possible lengths between 0 and 3 inches are possible for the shorter length (though if you set out to do the experiment you would be hard put to break it at a random, equally likely place, and very short lengths would probably not occur). There is, unfortunately, often a small difference between the way we talk about an experiment and the way we do it in practice, so that the two models of probability, the one based on reason and the one based on observation, do not always agree as closely as we would wish. It is one of the many annoying things which it is necessary to put up with in practice.

The most commonly used and easiest to understand distributions are those that are derived from equally likely events, that is, the probability of each possible outcome is the same as the probability of any other outcome. From such distributions other ones are easily

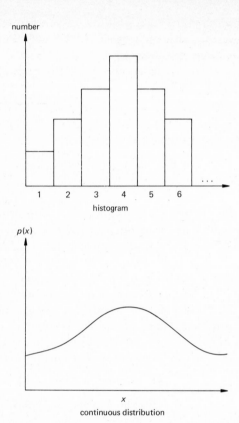

number

histogram

p(x)

x

continuous distribution

Figure 8-2

obtained. For example, suppose we want one probability A to be 37 percent and the other B to be 63 percent. If we select an equally likely two-decimal-digit number 00 to 99 and call it event A if the number is 00 to 36, and call it event B if the number is 37 to 99, we then have the two events A and B with the required probabilities.

The problem of counting word lengths produced a frequency for each word length. The results are often plotted as a histogram when the data are discrete numbers. When the data is continuous—that is, when any number can occur, not just discrete numbers—then the distribution takes the form of a smooth curve.

THE NEED FOR RANDOMNESS   8.6

We have already given some examples in which we needed random numbers from a distribution. In the inventory simulation we needed numbers to simulate the random delays in receiving the goods after the order was placed. This was not flat and uniform distribution, but rather somewhat bell-shaped, being zero at time zero, rising smoothly to a maximum and then falling off again towards zero for very long times. The exact shape to be used would, of course, depend on past experience with such delays (see Figure 8.3).

Another example of where we need to use random numbers is in simulating a supermarket checkout line. In such a simulation we can study the effect on the average waiting time of putting more checkout counters in the store. We could also study the variability of the average waiting time, the extremes of the waiting time, and similar effects. The mathematical discipline known as *queueing theory* provides some help in this matter. However, even this theory is not enought to handle many of the realistic parts of a simulation of the checkout waiting times of a supermarket. The changing load of customers has peculiar characteristics that are not easily expressed in simple mathematical formulas, although they are readily observed in practice.

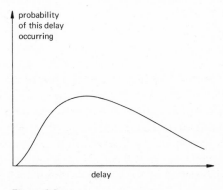

Figure 8-3

One of the earliest uses of random numbers was in the simulation of telephone traffic and its effects on a central office operation. Random numbers are needed to simulate the times at which customers will ask for service by picking up their telephone handset. Further random numbers (from different distributions) are needed for the time to complete the dialing, to make the connection, and for the "holding time" that the customer talks before hanging up and releasing the equipment for use by others.

One of the most common uses of random numbers is for the simulation of *noise*. Indeed, the word *noise* has gradually had its meaning extended from the acoustic noise that humans hear to cover many types of random variation. For example we speak of "random noise in a radar set," "noise on a telephone line," "noise in the measured value of a resistor." Indeed we sometimes use words like "noise in a production line" to mean the uncontrolled variability of the product being made by an apparently unchanging production line. The importance of the simulation of noise is that we often want to know more than what will happen under ideal conditions. We want to know what is likely to happen because of the inevitable noise in the system. We especially want to know what is the worst that is likely to happen and how often this worst behavior can be expected.

As an example, a manufacturer would like to know how the quality of hi-fi amplifiers will vary as they come off the production line, given the fact that he can control the accuracy of the individual components only within certain limits (which means that the components have a probability distribution in their values). He would also like to know how often a completely unacceptable amplifier will come from the line which will have to be scrapped as a total loss. He is also concerned about those that are actually sold, because too many poor ones will gradually ruin his reputation. To reduce this risk requires more care in the selection of the raw materials, and more inspection and control in the manufacturing process. The manufacturer can resort to computer simulations in order to understand in reasonable detail just what actions on his part can be expected to produce what results. The simulation, of course, implies that he knows a good deal about what he is doing, what he can control, what the distributions of the variable components are, and what the market will stand.

Random numbers are often used to select a random sample from a population. Thus in predicting election results the pollster selects a small sample of the entire population. Unless he is very careful to get a proper random sample, the results may be misleading, to say the least. Market surveys for purposes of predicting the probable success of a new product similarly use random samples from their population of possible buyers.

GENERATION OF RANDOM NUMBERS   8.7

If we are to use computers to solve many of the above types of problems, we are going to need some source of random numbers. At first, tables of random numbers were made and used. But, with the passage of time, we have preferred to generate random numbers in a machine as we need them. We generate random numbers by a fixed routine. This seeming contradiction has baffled many theoreticians but is simple to explain in practice. What we do is generate a sequence of numbers by a perfectly definite process, but the numbers, when examined without regard to the process used to make them, seem to be random (as tested by many different tests for randomness). One process for generating pseudo-random numbers on a k-bit machine is to pick

a) an $r = 8t - 3$; (for an arbitrary integer t)
b) and x_0 (an odd integer)

and then compute one after another the sequence of numbers

$$x_{n+1} = rx_n \pmod{2^k}$$

where $\pmod{2^k}$ means keep only the last k binary digits of the product. The pseudo-random numbers are $x_1, x_2, \dots$.

Let us illustrate this process for a $k = 5$-bit machine. We pick (using $t = 3$) $r = 8 \cdot 3 - 3 = 21$, and $x_0 = 1$. Then the first product is

$$
\begin{array}{l}
00001 = x_0 = 1 \\
\underline{10101 = r} \\
10101 = x_1 = 21
\end{array}
$$

The next product is

$$
\begin{array}{r}
10101 \\
10101 \\
\hline
10101 \\
101010 \\
1010100 \\
\hline
11001 = x_2 = 25
\end{array}
$$

Continuing in this way we get

$$
\begin{aligned}
00001 &= x_0 = 1 \\
10101 &= x_1 = 21 \\
11001 &= x_2 = 25 \\
01101 &= x_3 = 13 \\
10001 &= x_4 = 17 \\
00101 &= x_5 = 5 \\
01001 &= x_6 = 9 \\
11101 &= x_7 = 29 \\
00001 &= x_8 = 1
\end{aligned}
$$

and we observe that the numbers start to repeat at this point.

Note that we get one-fourth of the 32 possible 5-bit numbers before we repeat the cycle. This is the general rule for this formula: of the 2^k possible numbers in a k-bit machine, we get one-fourth of them and then repeat the cycle.

There is still a great deal of experimentation and testing of methods in the field of random number generation, but the results seem to be clear. With reasonable care, a simple formula can give a sequence of numbers that have most of the properties that are usually associated with the idea of random numbers. A typical formula will generate one-fourth of all the possible numbers that the machine can be expected to produce, and these numbers will be uniformly distributed over the whole range. In a 35-bit machine this means that the sequence will have $2^{33} \geqslant 8 \cdot 10^9$ distinct numbers before the sequence repeats, so the inherent periodicity is not much of a restriction.

Many more sophisticated tests can also be applied beyond the obvious one of uniform distribution, and the better formulas pass these tests. But it is a dangerous field for the amateur as it is easy to fall into a poor formula by carelessness. The number of people who have made this mistake is more than it is pleasant to contemplate.

In summary, the basic method is to generate pseudo-random numbers from a flat distribution (all equally likely) by a simple formula, and if necessary transform them later into other distributions to satisfy other conditions. The field is highly technical and we will not go into it any further.

AN ILLUSTRATIVE EXAMPLE FROM PSYCHOLOGY   8.8

The problem of teaching the nonspecialist what computers can do is, as we have repeatedly indicated, that of showing what has been done without getting enmeshed in a mass of details. To avoid being superficial and to give an accurate feeling for reality, it is necessary not only to sketch the broad flowcharts of a problem, but occasionally to show how to get close to machine details. An example which permits us to do this arose in a number of experiments run on a group of five persons whose task was to solve problems. The lines of communication between them were set up in various ways. Teams of five persons were brought to a round table that was partitioned into five sectors. Communication from one to another was permitted only by means of slips of paper put into communication channels that were varied from experiment to experiment. Thus by altering the communication channels, studies could be made of how a group organized itself to solve problems.

It was naturally assumed that the humans showed some intelligence in their attempts to solve the problems. However, it was proposed to simulate the situation on a machine using random behavior. Specifically, the simulation assumed that at each cycle time, each person made equally likely choices at random from among the channels available to him and then sent all the information that he had through the selected channel. In the simulation we counted how many cycles it took until everyone knew everything.

For the simulation we will need to generate equally likely random selections among 1, 2, 3, and 4 channels of communication, depending on the number available to each individual. Suppose that we have available a source of two decimal-digit random numbers 00, 01, ... , 99. If we need two choices, we can simply divide the given random number by 2 and use the remainder, 0 or 1, as the basis for the choice. For three choices, we throw away the number 99 every time it appears and select another random number. Having now one of the set 00, 01, ... , 98, we divide the number by 3 and take the remainder. For the case 4 we proceed much as we did for the case 2. Thus we can make a small program to provide a random, equally likely choice among any of 1, 2, 3, or 4 choices.

For storage of the information that each individual in the experiment has at each cycle, we assign a 5-bit number per person, using a 0 in each place when he has the information from the corresponding person and a 1 when he does not have the information. At the start, of course, he has a 0 in his own position and a 1 elsewhere. At the start of a cycle, he selects a random channel from those available to him and sends down it all that he knows. At the same time he receives one or more messages that update his information.

A check is then made to see if the problem is done (each person has all 0s), and if not, the cycle number is increased by 1 and the process is repeated. At the completion, when each person has all 0s (knows everything), the number of cycles used represents the "time to solve the problem." By running the simulation many times for each configuration of the communication channels, we can find not only the average number of cycles to get all the information to everyone, but also the variability on the number of cycles.

Let us repeat the point, however. We do not in the least pretend that humans are acting at random. We do claim that in this case the simulation of human behavior *as if* each person acted in a random manner gave useful indications for the real case.

AN EXAMPLE OF ION VELOCITY DISTRIBUTION   8.9

Another example of the use of random numbers in a problem involved a study of the distribution of velocities of ions (charged particles) trickling through a gas under a constant accelerating force. An ion collides occasionally with a relatively fixed molecule of the gas and rebounds at some angle with some loss of velocity. To simulate such a process we need random numbers from suitable distributions for each of the following:

1. the random angle of recoil
2. the time to the next collision
3. the energy loss due to inelastic collision

Each of these individual formulas was known from the classical theory of ion-molecule collisions.

We therefore simulated one ion going through 10,000 collisions, and from this history it was comparatively easy to find the distributions of the velocities both along and perpendicular to the direction of the acceleration. The results proved to be remarkably accurate, and the form of the computed answer suggested the nature of the answer to a theoretician. Knowing the form of the answer, he was then able to get the result directly from the theory.

MONTE CARLO METHODS   8.10

The idea of simulating a random process by using appropriate random numbers is an old one. As we mentioned previously, perhaps the first use on a large scale was in the early telephone simulations of traffic in a telephone central office. Here we need random numbers for the time that a call is started, further random numbers for estimating the time to complete the call and ring the phone, more random numbers for the answering or nonanswering of the phone, and finally random numbers for the time the conversation runs until the parties hang up and free the equipment for others to use.

A less obvious example is the proposal of the French naturalist, Buffon (1773), who observed that if a needle of length l is tossed at random on a flat level surface with lines spaced one unit away from each other, then the probability of the needle crossing the line is given by

$$P = \frac{2l}{\pi}$$

for l less than 1 in length.

We can invert the equation, as he observed, and experimentally determine the value of π by tossing the needle. This is a fine method for finding out that π is around 3. It is possible to find (by a good deal of care and labor) that π is around 3.1. But it is not very practical to try for 3.14159.

The colorful name *Monte Carlo* was originally given to problems which had no random component but which could be recast so that they would, as in the above computation of π. The name is now often applied as well to problems which have a naturally occurring random element.

If we restrict the name to cases where the answer could be found by direct methods, but a random method is used instead, we find an enormous amount of literature, but very few useful results. On the other hand, for problems with naturally occurring random elements, these random methods have helped a great deal.

RANDOM NUMBERS IN GAME PLAYING   8.11

There are a number of uses for random numbers in the field of game playing. When a machine is playing a human opponent, say, in checkers, the human, by playing small variations in his game, can probe the machine's formula for possible weaknesses. Having found one, he can systematically exploit it and win game after game. To prevent this, most game strategies incorporate a random choice among a number of the apparently better moves, so the human trying to play exactly the same game again finds that the machine introduces small variations from time to time and gradually the game being played diverges from the last one. When done properly, this protects the machine's formula from exploitation and makes it rather difficult for the outsider playing the machine to find out what the formula actually is.

In another game-playing situation (see Chapter 14), random numbers are used to let the machine play both sides of a game, using different formulas. After a number of games the formula that is probably better will be indicated by the high number of wins. Without the random element in the game, there would only be two distinct games, depending on whether the first or the second formula had the opening move.

Still another use of random numbers is in the attack on a problem which we do not know how to solve. If we make random trials, the argument goes, we will sooner or later hit upon the lucky combination and produce the solution. The reasoning behind this is a lot like the famous "monkeys and the typewriters" story. In the story it is asserted that if some monkeys are set down before some typewriters, sooner or later (meaning much later in practice) the monkeys will type out all the books in the British Museum in the order in which they occur in the card catalog. The proof goes along the lines that sooner or later a monkey will type the first letter correctly. Indeed, waiting long enough, this will happen arbitrarily often. Of the times that the first letter is typed correctly, there is a small chance that the second correct letter will immediately follow. Considering those cases in which they get the first two letters right, there is a probability that the third letter will be correct. And so it goes. Of course, it is an ideal experiment. The monkeys and the typewriters, or even the universe itself, will probably not last long enough to get even a few paragraphs correct, but theoretically it is true that it will happen sometime in the infinitude of all time.

STATISTICS   8.12

There is no simple definition of statistics that will satisfy the majority of statisticians. One aspect of statistics can be expressed in the following way. In probability theory we are given the basic, underlying probabilities of simple events and we are asked to compute the probabilities of various compound events. Thus probability theory can answer such questions as "In tossing a well-balanced coin 7 times, what is the probability of getting at least 5 heads?" Statistics, on the other hand, starts with the probabilities (usually observations) of compound events and tries to estimate the probabilities of the simple underlying mechanisms. A typical problem in statistics would be to estimate the probable bias of a coin, given a set of observations. It is characteristic of statistics that the answer given often has a degree of uncertainty associated with it expressed as a probability. Thus we can say that a coin *probably* has a certain, stated bias, not that it has exactly that bias.

A second aspect of statistics is the organization of a mass of data into a more compact form for presentation to others. For example, in the simulation of the psychological experiment (Section 8.8) 200 cases of each possible configuration of the communication channels were run and tabulated. The result for a single configuration was a set of 200 problem solution times, t_i. To summarize this mass of data we com-

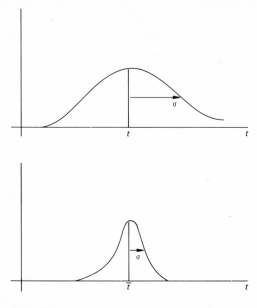

Figure 8-4

puted the mean (average) $\bar{t}$ and the variance (variability about the mean), which is defined as

$$\sigma^2 = (t_1 - \bar{t})^2 + (t_2 - \bar{t})^2 + ... + (t_{200} - \bar{t})^2$$

The variance measures roughly the *spread* of the distribution about the mean (see Figure 8-4). The mean and the variance are the two numbers most commonly used to describe a distribution. Obviously, these two numbers cannot tell all there is to know about a distribution, but they do provide a convenient way of comparing various distributions.

A third aim of (at least some) statistics is to obtain "insight" into the system, mechanism, or phenomenon that is producing the data. This aspect of statistics is much more an art than a science, and is therefore hard to describe to the outsider.

Statistics is a very highly developed field and its sound application requires years of study and practice. All that can be done here is to indicate some of its features. The characteristic feature, as we have already indicated, is that the result of a statistical study is not *certainty* but rather a statement that *probably* something is true, often with a given measure of the probability. It is customary to express the degree of certainty in terms of *confidence level*. A 5 percent confidence level means that, on the average, once in 20 times the answer will be wrong. Sometimes 3 percent and even 1 percent confidence levels are used, but they can be very expensive, both in the amount of data it is necessary to gather to give that assurance, and in the number of times one will fail to act because he did not achieve the level wanted.

This last point brings up the fact that there are various kinds of errors you can make when acting on statistical predictions. You can take action based on the prediction and be correct; you can take the action predicted and be wrong; but you can also fail to take action when you should; and you can fail to take action and be right in so doing. The average person often does not recognize the importance of the error of failing to take action when he should. They want to play things safe and wait until they are sure—but in real life you can rarely hope to be sure.

When computers are used in applying statistics to a situation and the result is bad, it is obviously not the machine that is at fault. It is the statistical tests and the inherent risk of action that must take the blame.

SUMMARY   8.13

We have introduced three kinds of probability: frequency, logical, and subjective. And we have given some examples of the use of the first two types in a number of widely different situations. The third type will be examined more closely in Chapter 12.

The generation of random numbers to simulate random processes on the computer is a central idea. From what is in fact a perfectly definite process of generating the random numbers we appear to get the effect of random behavior. The use of randomness is one of the central ideas of the statistical applications that one reads about, and therefore it is necessary to understand just what is going on before accepting the claims that the computer used a random process to obtain a certain result. The result is no more valid than the underlying ideas and does not depend on the amount of computer time used or the quality of the output printing.

CHAPTER 9

Complex Computer by G. R. Stibitz (Bell Telephone Laboratories, 1940)
Courtesy of Bell Telephone Laboratories.

The Computer
As an Experimental Tool

This chapter examines the use of the computer

1. before doing an experiment
2. during an experiment
3. after an experiment
4. in place of an experiment
5. as a source of new types of experiments

The first three are fairly straightforward, not very exciting, and will be disposed of rapidly. Only the last two are of major intellectual interest. But before examining these we need to make a digression on the topic of how digital computers handle information in the form of signals and data from the real world, and the consequences of how this is done.

ANALOG SIGNALS AND ANALOG COMPUTERS   9.1

Many of the quantities we are concerned with in daily life appear as continuously varying signals rather than as a stream of discrete numbers. Thus we think of the heart beat pressure, the brain wave voltages, the position of a moving object, the brightness of a star, the sound pressure on the ear drum, and so on, as continuously varying in time. They can take on any value in a given range. Such information is called *analog data*, as contrasted to data represented by a stream of numbers, called *digital data*. Digital data take on only discrete values represented by numbers that have limited precision (that is, they have a limited number of places in the number representation).

There are a number of different kinds of computers that are loosely called *analog computers* and work essentially with analog signals. We shall now examine some of them briefly.

Perhaps the most commonly known analog computer is the slide rule, which represents the values of numbers by lengths (usually the length is proportional to the logarithm of the number). However, most of the larger analog computers are electronic and use a voltage to represent a signal (number) in the *differential analyzer*. This technology grew largely out of the gun directors of the Second World War, although the basic ideas were developed in a series of mechanical differential analyzers built by Vannevar Bush at MIT starting in the 1920s. These machines are designed to solve "ordinary differential equations," though they will do some other problems as well. They tend (1) to have components that are individually accurate to a few parts per 10,000, and (2) to operate all the components in parallel at the same time rather than sequentially, as does a digital machine.

Hybrid computers are a combination of both analog and digital machines. They are an attempt to get the best of both types of machines while avoiding the worst. How the balance comes out is an open question. In any case, hybrid computers are not of direct interest in this book, and they will not be discussed further.

ANALOG-TO-DIGITAL CONVERSION 9.2

Since many of the signals that we wish to process on a digital computer occur originally as an analog signal, it is necessary to convert them to digital form. The conversion is usually done by examining the analog signal at regular intervals (sampling) and creating a number which is close to the value of the analog signal at that moment. Such a device is called an *analog-to-digital converter*.

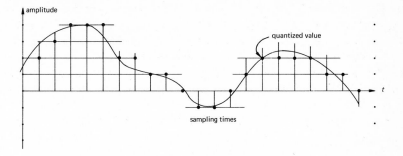

Figure 9-1

To decide how many samples per unit of time (usually one second) to take, we reason as follows. If the signal is slowly changing, then it is foolish to take thousands of samples per second. On the other hand, if the signal varies rapidly, then it is necessary to take many samples per second if we are to keep up with (follow) the changes of the signal. This reasoning can be formalized very precisely. We will return to the question of sampling rate a little later. At present there are analog-to-digital converters which will convert more than 300,000 samples per second. As might be expected, the more conversions per second, the more the equipment is apt to cost, and hence lower sampling rates are used whenever possible.

Besides the frequency of conversion there is also the question of how *accurately* the analog signal is to be represented. That is, how many different numbers are going to be used to represent the sample? In other words, how many bits are there going to be in the digital representation of the sample? Typically, analog-to-digital converters give 10 to 15 bits of accuracy, which is from about 1 part in a thousand to 1 part in 32,000. Again, the more the precision, the more you pay.

The analog signal is *quantized in time* by the process of taking samples, and is *quantized in amplitude (height)* by the conversion from the continuously varying analog signal to the discrete signal (Figure 9-1). The effect of the amplitude quantizing is equivalent to adding a small amount of noise to the signal. This has much less effect on most problems than the average person thinks it will, so that fairly inaccurate digitizers (converters) are often used.

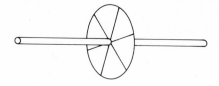

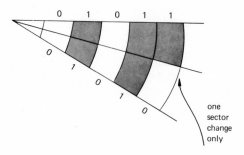

Figure 9-2   Gray code.

THE GRAY CODE   9.4

We have frequently used examples from the theory of the representation of information to show how highly developed is that body of knowledge. The so-called Gray code often used in analog-to-digital converters is another such example.

Imagine a rotating shaft whose angular position at various equally spaced times is to be represented by a stream of numbers. We can picture a wheel rotating on a shaft with the position measured either electrically via brushes or optically via photo cells (Figure 9-2). The quantization in angle is done by dividing the wheel into sectors and scanning the sector that happens to be in the reading position at the appropriate sampling time. Thus each position of the wheel has a corresponding sector at the scanning position.

But suppose that the wheel has part of one sector and part of another beneath the reading device at the same time. What will be read? If the position number of the sector were encoded in the binary number system, then passing, say, from sector 15 to sector 16, we would pass from reading 01111 to 10000. In the confusion of changing all 5 bits almost anything might be read out. Thus the binary number system with its occasional multiple changes as you go from one number to the next is not a satisfactory form for representing the angle of the rotating shaft.

The Gray code is one way of associating angle positions with symbols in a binary notation (*not* the binary number notation) so that in passing from sector to sector only *one position* in the binary representation changes. Thus the error that can arise from straddling two sectors is minimized, because the converter will read out one of the two numbers representing the straddled sectors in all cases.

Table 9.3-1

decimal (shaft position)	Gray	equivalent binary
0	000	000
1	001	001
2	011	010
3	010	011
4	110	100
5	111	101
6	101	110
7	100	111

As an example of the Gray code, consider a 3-bit (eight shaft positions) read-out from an analog-to-digital converter shown in Table 9.3-1. There are simple ways of going between the Gray and binary number codes, but the details are not important here.

THE EFFECT OF SAMPLING 9.4

It is difficult to discuss precisely the effects of sampling without using a great deal of mathematics. However, one of the general effects is common knowledge to TV viewers and to moviegoers who are watching, in both cases, "sampled pictures" at about 20 frames per second.

Consider a typical Western movie in which the stage coach starts up. At first the wheels turn more and more rapidly, but then they seem to slow down, stop, and then start to go backwards. As the coach goes still faster the wheels again stop and then appear to again go forward.

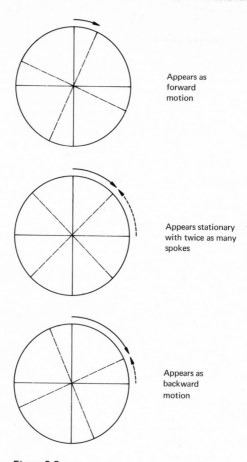

Appears as
forward
motion

Appears stationary
with twice as many
spokes

Appears as
backward
motion

Figure 9-3

Seldom does the stage coach go fast enough to repeat this cycle many times, though it is conceptually possible to happen as often as required.

Why does this effect occur? It is simply due to the sampling. As the wheel starts up (see Figure 9-3) you see the spokes advancing each frame as expected, but when the wheel is going fast enough so that the spoke in the next frame is exactly half of the way around to the next spoke, then the wheel seems to stand still with twice as many spokes as it really has. When going faster still, the spoke in successive frames is

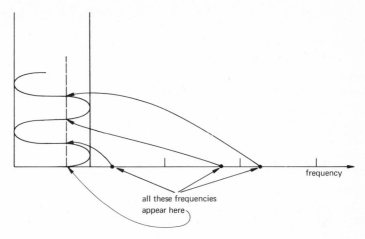

frequency

all these frequencies
appear here

Figure 9-4

slightly behind where the next spoke was, so the wheel appears to the eye to be going backwards. When it is going so fast that the wheel has rotated exactly the distance of one full spoke during the time between pictures, then again it seems to be standing still. And so it goes.

This same phenomenon is also seen in the use of stroboscopic devices. If we look at some rotating machinery using a flashing light, then with the proper rate of flashing the machinery seems to be standing still. If we flash at slightly less than the period of a full rotation, then each flash finds the machinery having done one full rotation plus a small amount more, and we see only the small amount more. By properly choosing the rate of flashing we can make the machinery appear to go at any speed we wish, including backwards. This phenomenon is occasionally seen under fluorescent lights.

Thus the effect of sampling on a periodic phenomenon is to make a fast period appear as a much slower one. This is called *aliasing*: one frequency goes under the name of another frequency. The crucial sampling rate is at twice the highest frequency. If the sampling rate is greater than this, then all frequencies appear correctly. If the sampling rate is less, then we get less than two samples per cycle for some frequencies and they appear as a lower frequency. Figure 9-4 gives a schematic of the aliasing that occurs. Any frequency on the "folded" strip of frequencies appears as if it has the frequency that it lies over.

We are now in a position to be more precise about what sampling rates we must have. If, for example, we want to follow music up to 5000 cycles per second (440 cycles per second is middle A, 880 is one octave above, 1760 two octaves above, and 3520 is three octaves above) then we will need at least 10,000 samples per second. Reasoning the other way, if we choose the sampling rate, then we can find the highest frequency that will appear properly, and all higher frequencies will appear aliased as lower frequencies (they are *not* removed).

The same kind of argument can be applied to the recording in digital form of brain waves and heart beats. We must know the highest frequencies that we have to follow before we fix the sampling rate. We also need to consider that if there are any higher frequencies than these, then they should be filtered out *before* the sampling. Otherwise, by their aliased values they will contaminate the lower frequencies.

DIGITAL-TO-ANALOG CONVERSION   9.5

It is frequently desirable, or even necessary, to convert digital signals (a stream of numbers) to an analog signal, which is obviously the reverse process to that we have been considering. The process is conceptually simple. A voltage appropriate in size to each digit position of the first number is emitted whenever there is a 1 in that position, and it is not emitted when there is a 0. These voltages are then added together and the sum represents the number. The same is then done for the next number, and so on.

It is necessary to put a little smoothing (by means of a device called a filter) to remove the sudden jumps between successive values of the stream of numbers in order to produce a smooth output. If the smoothing is properly done, there are no "back-aliased" high frequencies appearing in the output that were not in the stream of numbers originally.

Both A → D and D → A converters are needed in hybrid computers to get to and from the analog and digital parts of the computer. They are also used in many other systems, such as flight trainers and space shot simulators.

MUSIC   9.6

Production of music has received a great deal of attention from people who are interested in computers. Their efforts may be divided, mainly, into two approaches: programming a computer to compose music, and simulating musical sounds by computer. (Analysis of music has also been done to some extent.)

Probably the first composed music to achieve national attention was a composition, based in part on the use of random numbers, called Push-Button Bertha (1956) and played briefly on radio stations on the West Coast.

Much more serious were the efforts by Hiller and Isaacson of the University of Illinois to compose music on a computer. Their efforts resulted in the *Illiac Suite* (*Experimental Music*, Hiller and Isaacson, McGraw-Hill, 1959). What they did, briefly, was to write programs that described the rules of composition of various musical forms, and let the machine see if the next note chosen at random met the required rules. If it did, the note was accepted, and if not, the note was rejected and another trial was made. If enough failures occurred in a row, the program backed up and re-did one or more of the previous notes.

Some of their results were organized into the *Illiac Suite* (named after the Illiac computer on which the computing was done) and was played by a local musical group. Later it was played by the University band.

Composing by, or more accurately, with the aid of, a computer is popular in some circles. The possiblity of random composition is especially attractive to many modern composers, John Cage being perhaps the leading exponent of the use of random effects in music composition.

Computer-made Music

Computer-made music should be distinguished from computer-composed music. Further, it is necessary to distinguish various forms of making music (sounds). Two approaches to using the new electronic capabilities that we now have for making sounds are the French School of *Musique Concrete*, which uses natural sounds recorded on a tape recorder as a basis but alters and regroups and selects various parts by electronic technique, and a German group, which uses electronic sounds that are not originally natural. Still other people use specially made electronic equipment to form the sounds, such as the Moog instrument.

The computer-made music we shall discuss is produced *directly* from the computer in the following manner. The computer calculates a stream of numbers and these are converted via a digital-to-analog converter (plus a simple smoothing filter) to a sound track that is later played on a tape recorder.

To understand how complex sounds can be produced by such a system, consider what happens at the opening of your ear during a concert. There is at any instant effectively a single air pressure at each one of the two ear openings. This air pressure varies with time and is the sum of sounds made by all the musical instruments, the echos of the concert hall, the coughs of your neighbors, etc. All the sounds are added together (except at very loud sound levels) to produce a specific air pressure at any single instant. Whether you hear this directly or whether it is converted by a microphone to an electrical voltage and then recorded on a tape to be played later, it is a single, time-varying function (one such function for each ear). Thus on the magnetic tape of a tape recorder there is a magnetic signal which varies from place to place along the tape and is in some sense equivalent to the air pressure. Running the tape past the playing head of a tape recorder produces a time-varying voltage very much like the original time-varying air pressure. This voltage activates the loud speaker which produces the variations in the air pressure you finally hear.

If we produce numbers in the computer that correspond to the samples of the amplitude of the voltage that corresponds to the sound, we can make a sound track directly without using any musical instruments at all. To do this a program is written for the computer that includes a musical score for one or more instruments, and descriptions of the characteristics of musical instruments (attack, overtone, and vibrato pattern). This single program, written only once, then computes numbers which are put on a digital tape. This digital tape, when passed through a digital-to-analog converter, makes the magnetic tape that is played on a standard tape recorder to produce the "music" you hear.

The rate of computing the numbers is not important (except for the cost) since we can take as long as we please to compute them. But when it comes to running the digital tape through the digital-to-analog converter, it is necessary to do this at a fixed rate, preferably at the rate that the final music is to occur (though obviously we can do it at half the rate and later play the tape at twice the speed if we please). Thus only the digital-to-analog converter needs to function at a rapid rate.

For example, to produce a pure tone we would write a program that computed the values of the sine function at a very small spacing.

The pitch of the pure tone you heard would depend on the spacing of the angles used in the samples of the sine function.

With this technique for producing sounds the composer has at his command *any sound* that can theoretically exist, and not merely those that natural instruments can make. And if we distinguish between the composer and the conductor, then the conductor can go over a passage as often as he wants and precisely control the changes until he has exactly what he wants. Thus in some sense we have reached the ultimate in the matter of technically producing music. We have in a very real sense reached perfect control over any sound that can possibly exist.

Where we lack control is in determining what sounds to make to have the desired effect. The sudden opening of the new world of all possible sounds leaves us in doubt about which ones to choose.

Most of the people who have responded to this new step forward (backward so far as some people are concerned, to be sure) have been engineers who are not basically musicians, and what they have done with the new tool is about what you would expect from them.

Therefore, before criticising the new "music" (if you will pardon the word), remember:

1. The composing was probably done by an amateur musician and not a great composer. How well would music that you composed sound?

2. Most of the currently classical music was regarded as a "scandal" when it first appeared, and it was often a generation or two before people learned to appreciate and like it.

3. When you hear Oriental music, you realize that a different form of music requires experience and perhaps training to appreciate. Electronic music also probably falls in this category.

At present (1970), the most frequent occurrence of computer-made music and sounds is in TV commercials.

AN AUDIO ILLUSION   9.7

There is a class of pictures that are called *visual illusions*. They are figures that appear to be one thing but are in fact somewhat different. A theory of hearing that was current some years ago suggested to a

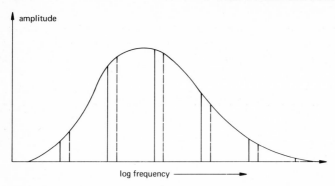

Figure 9-5

research psychologist that by adapting the computer technique for making music he could test out the theory by producing an *auditory illusion.*

What he programmed was, in effect, a sequence of complex tones, one sound after the other, that gave the illusion of continually rising, but was in fact not doing this. No amount of verbal description can convey this remarkable illusion. However, let us look at how he did it. Figure 9-5 shows an "envelope" under which the amplitude (strength, intensity) of the tones were kept. The first tone and its harmonics was the sound with the amplitudes as shown. The frequencies are plotted on a logarithmic scale (which means that equal steps along the horizontal axis correspond to going up one more octave, i.e., doubling the frequency). Thus the first complex tone was the sum of a very weak fundamental, several stronger overtones, and higher overtones again decaying in amplitude. The next complex tone was made by moving each component of the tone up 1/12 of the distance to the next octave (dotted lines). When heard, this tone appears to be higher in frequency than the first tone. The following tone moved up another 1/12—each time, of course, keeping the amplitudes under the envelope. Thus the lower frequencies tended to be amplified on successive steps, while the higher ones tended to be weakened.

After 12 such steps forward, the note is right back where it was. A new lowest frequency came in at so low an amplitude that it could not be noticed by the human ear, and the highest frequency was lost at a time when it was too weak to be heard. In a loose sense the tones went around in a circle.

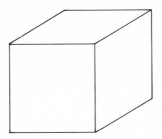

Figure 9-6

In this example we have used the computer to make a tape to illustrate a theory of hearing. It would have been very hard to make such a precise and complex tape in the conventional manner. In this experiment we are learning about humans and how they hear tones. This is one of the many bases for the claim that computers are not merely tools for the scientist and the engineer to use to study their special fields, but rather they are tools that can be used to learn about ourselves. Computers are tools for the humanists to use as well as for the scientists.

DEPTH PERCEPTION 9.8

Similar to the use of the computer to produce sounds that reveal how humans perceive sound is another set of experiments designed to study how humans perceive depth.

Many computers can produce a microfilm output, originally used mainly to produce graphs but capable of making a wide variety of pictures. The microfilm can portray lines or isolated spots. Many people are aware that pictures they see reproduced are, on close examination, a collection of isolated spots of varying size and darkness. Thus the microfilm output can be used to produce pictures in this form to be viewed by humans. The information to make the picture comes from digitized information in the computer.

The central problem in depth perception studies is that of separating the actual perception of depth from learned responses. Thus if I present you with the conventional picture of a cube (Figure 9-6), you see it in three dimensions because you have learned to associate the

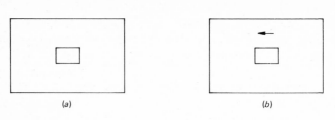

Figure 9-7

plane figure with a three-dimensional object. In fact, though, the lines are on a single plane and cannot be a 3-dimensional figure.

The experimenter, being aware of the computer and its possibilities, decided to use the random number generator and the microfilm output to produce 10,000 spots of random brightness. By making the same picture twice (Figure 9-7), except that the second time a central rectangular area is displaced slightly, and then viewing it in a stereopticon, the appearance of depth is produced in the same form as it appears to the human eye. Because such random figures have no "learned response," the researcher has an ideal tool for experimentally studying how humans perceive depth.

He can study displacements that produce three or more levels of perception—lacy patterns rather than regular regions of displacement. He can study the effect of having one picture 10 percent larger than the other, or 10 percent brighter than the other.

In each case he can study how difficult it is to "see" as measured by the time to see the illusion, how stable the illusion is, and so on.

In both the acoustic and visual cases, the computer is providing the experimental tool to study the functioning of man himself.

FURTHER ILLUSTRATIONS   9.11

The first use of a computer that often comes to mind, and one of the main uses in the earliest days of large-scale digital computers, is that of reducing the data from an experiment. Often there is a great deal of computing to be done to get the desired quantities from the raw data that an experiment yields. Every space missile uses a great deal of this kind of computing. The time at which a measurement is made needs to be transformed, via the orbit information, into where the missile was when the data was measured. A fair-sized space experiment can keep a big computer going full time doing this sort of data reduction. Indeed, just keeping track of what is floating around in space requires a great deal of computing. Each radar measurement needs to be identified, using past orbital data, with the particular object, and occasionally the orbital elements need to be refined in terms of the latest observations.

While this use of computers still occupies a great deal of machine time, we shall ignore it from now on because it is essentially dull and uninteresting, though often hard to do.

The use of a computer *before* an experiment is coming into more use. Perhaps a good illustration of this is my first experience with large-scale computation, the calculation of what a proposed design of an atomic bomb could be expected to produce when it was actually tried. From the calculated results of one trial design the experts could make judgments as to how to design the next try. In this fashion they gradually came to a design that worked. The results, at least to me, were surprisingly accurate when compared with the actual field trial at Almagordo—however disturbing the whole aim and application.

In this situation there is no possibility of doing small-scale experiments. Either you try out a full-sized bomb or you don't try one at all. Sometimes before an experiment it is possible to do the traditional laboratory or pilot experiment, but these have been found to be costly in time and money. Thus the computer is used instead to simulate the experiment. The computer serves as a basis for the pilot study. For instance, in the current space shots there are extensive simulations of the situation long before an actual field trial is made. Indeed, the use of computers before an experiment to simulate what will happen is so widespread and successful that the very technique of experimentation has been altered. Simulation plays a prominent role in almost all large-scale experiments in which there is a sufficient body of knowledge to provide even a poor model.

The possibilities of this approach have not yet been exhausted, and we are still learning new things about how to carry on the art of simulation. However, we shall leave the subject here, merely noting that this use consumes a large part of the capacity of many machines.

The use of the computer as a control device *during* the experiment is gradually coming into more prominence. At first the computer was used merely to gather the data from an experiment. Gradually it was also used to direct the set up, and check out the equipment before the experiment was run. Sometimes it was used to cycle the equipment through a series of repetitive experiments and to supply the input pulses. We will examine such uses in more detail later.

SYNTHETIC WORLDS   9.10

I have now started down a path that I expect most readers will not wish to follow to the end, but will prefer to drop off at some point along the way. Indeed, I am not sure how far I believe in it myself, but let me present the vision. There are three distinct questions to be asked about the path:

1. How far can we go?
2. How far will we go?
3. How far should we go?

Let me introduce the idea of a "synthetic world." By this I shall mean a world that finds its main inspiration not in the real world but in the mental world. Games are good examples of synthetic worlds. As a first example, consider the game of chess. No one really pretends that it is a model of warfare. It is a game that is amusing to play. The characteristics that I am interested in are

1. The rules are explicitly known and are inherently simple.
2. The object of the game is also clearly known.
3. How to combine the elementary rules to achieve the stated goal is not known; rather, it is so complex as to defy (up to now) any reasonable analysis.

Bridge is another game that is really a synthetic world. In addition to the stated rules there is a random element whose characteristic (uniform distribution over all possible hands) is supposed to be closely achieved by a moderate amount of shuffling. (We will examine more of the details of machines playing games in Chapter 14).

Indeed, almost all games fall in the class I am calling a synthetic world, and I should like to dwell for a moment on the powerful attraction such synthetic worlds have for many people. They can be very attractive indeed, and for some people can occupy a major part of their lives.

Perhaps the ultimate game is programming a computing machine. Here, again, all the rules are known in advance, but unlike other games, the object, producing a particular working program, changes from game to game. Thus programming offers the devotee an almost infinite number of variations on the basic game. The rules stay the same, but the objective of the game is constantly being changed from problem to problem. If you have any doubt of the truth of my remarks you have only to watch or talk to a professional programmer for a while to find that often he really has only the slightest interest in the use of the program that he writes. All he cares about is being given a clearly stated goal and then being let alone to work out how, using the moves allowed by the machine, to get from the stated problem to the working program. When the program works, his interest usually vanishes. While there is some ultimate reality both in the machine and the paper he uses, as well as in the use the program is to be put, his major activity has only the most tenuous connection with the real world: it is a genuine example of activity in a synthetic world.

Whether we choose to view theoretical physics as a game or not is not of importance here. Suffice it to say that some people regard it as a game and some do not. Much the same can be said in other fields of science.

Having made clear, I hope, the main characteristics of what I mean by a synthetic world, as well as its enormous attraction for many people, let me get back to the path I wish to take you down. Obviously, it is the path to synthetic worlds, but let us recall how far we have already gone. Evidently the two experiments, acoustic and visual, I cited before are a start toward the synthetic world. In both cases the stimuli used were not naturally occurring ones. They were highly artificial, and their possibility rested very much on the existence of computers. Furthermore, the possibility of imagining the experiments rested heavily on an acquaintance with computers and their capabilities. The example (Section 8.8) of the computer study of a group of five persons solving a problem jointly is another synthetic experiment.

In many ways the random model shed more light than did the actual experiments (insofar as it was a study of the effect of communication channels on solution time). This example I am sure many of you will go along with, though we are still farther down the path to a synthetic world.

The next example I wish to take up involves the same psychologist. One day I said to him that if he would define a tribe of Martians, with every one being identical or else having statistically distributed characteristics, whichever he chose, I would simulate the Martians' behavior on a computer and we could then study the basic problem of "how characteristics of the individual are transformed through group interactions into different, group characteristics." Suppose we had studied this for 5 years or so, with an increasingly larger group, until we felt that we had a grasp on the basic question of how group interactions transform individual characteristics into group characteristics. I claim, and you may not care to go along with me this far, that we would know much more than we now do about such problems as the behavior of committees, mob psychology, corporate behavior, etc., where it is clear that the group behavior often does not resemble what any one individual would do alone. In short, I am claiming that having studied a completely synthetic world of interactions between fictitious Martians we would be better off than spending the same effort studying real people in real situations. It is not that we have no need of real data, but rather that we already have a lot of data, and in complex situations real data can often lead to more confusion than clarity.

PHILOSOPHY   9.11

This raises the awkward question of how much more real data we need to gather. If we want to continue on the classical path of science and to control the exterior world (which is the path science has been following), then I believe that we will still need to gather new, real data, though perhaps not in the quantity that we have in the past. But there are other paths we can follow, ones that do not require the gathering of lots of real data. There are paths that are more closely related to our interior lives, where we already have all too much data.

Before you dismiss the concept of ignoring the external world, stop to reflect the role that music has played in the human life. It is not based primarily on the real world. Tone poems and similar material are not closely connected with reality in spite of what is claimed. No, music is mainly engaged in for the private internal pleasure of humans, and there is no pretense that it is related in any serious way with the external world.

Remember the three questions: How far can we go into synthetic worlds and simply ignore reality? How far will we go? How far should we go? We already have a lot of control over the external world, and even if we gradually shift our major attention in the future to synthetic internal worlds, we need not completely abandon the real world. It is not an all-or-nothing, it is a question of degree.

Well, how far can we go? I say we can go very far, so far that the major attention of almost everyone could be involved in synthetic worlds that give him pleasure (just as some of us are now deeply involved with music, games, etc.) After all, what limits us? With computers providing vast, as yet unimagined synthetic worlds of pleasures to explore, why engage in the already marginal exploration of this all too unsatisfactory real world? I believe there is potentially no limit on how far we can go if we wish.

How far will we go? Again, recall how far many of us have already gone into music, games, and programming for the love of programming with only the slightest regard for utility. Recall the attractiveness of a world in which all the basic rules are known, where the goals may be set arbitrarily and cleanly, and where the whole challenge is in the very complexity of the problem of getting from the start to the finish. Don't sell the human too short in his willingness to enjoy life. With the ability to make synthetic worlds to fit his desires, far beyond what amateur daydreaming can do, worlds where there is a real intellectual challenge and a sense of accomplishment that transcends any reward that mere daydreaming can offer—think of how far many people will choose to go.

Lastly, how far should we go? Here we are on moral and ethical grounds. I, with my strong Puritan training that so often gets in the way of enjoying life, naturally believed at first that we should shun the path of pleasures, of enjoyment for its own sake, just as many of us believe that the path of drugs used for pleasure should be avoided. But remember, these beliefs were appropriate for the world when there was a lack of control over the external forces. Is it so appropriate now? And even if it is appropriate now, will it be in the future? I can only wonder at and speculate on how much previous conditioning has produced my instinctive judgment that warns of danger. I can say, however, that every time I rethink the question I go a bit further down the pleasure path than I did the previous time.

What has all this to do with the topic of this chapter, the use of the computer as an experimental tool? Simply this: at first approach, one naturally has a very limited vision of what the computer can do as an experimental tool. I took you rapidly through the obvious uses, before, during, and after an experiment. I went more slowly through the region where the computer provides a new tool for doing new experiments in the more or less classical fields of experimentation. Finally, I ventured some speculation as to the use of the computer to explore unconventional worlds, worlds that are more internally oriented than the usual externally objective world. In the past we have demanded external verification. Even in introspection we rarely venture far in psychology without trying to gain some external evidence for the reported internal states.

But there are human activities that have to a great extent remained outside the main stream of science. Art, music, and literature come readily to mind. Such activities have always attracted human attention because of the inherent internal pleasure they give. Another example is "logical pleasure" in, among other places, mathematics. It seems to me that we will find that the computer provides us with a tool to explore our personal pleasures by allowing us to create what I have called, for lack of better words, synthetic worlds. When I say that computers may provide a major tool for creating and exploring synthetic worlds of pleasure, remember that curiosity, both about others and about oneself, is one of the major human characteristics. We have traditionally honored those who have pursued their strong drive of curiosity about how things operate, we have honored those who have been capable of creating new music, paintings, poetry, and literature even when it has had no economic contribution to make in the form of control of the external world. Are you now so sure that computers cannot, will not, or should not be used to create and explore private worlds of pleasure?

SUMMARY   9.12

The use of the computer in the real world of physical signals requires converting the analog signals to digital form, both by sampling the signal, thereby causing an inevitable aliasing, and by quantizing the signal with its corresponding errors.

The computer is used in many ways in experimental work, not only before, during, and after an experiment, but more and more it is used in place of actual experiments in the real world. This simulation of reality raises the questions of how far we can, will, and should go in this direction of replacing reality with simulations. Hopefully the chapter has also caused the reader to think a good deal more about these synthetic worlds that are now opening up to us, worlds more centered within ourselves than have in the past been regarded as suitable for experimentation in science.

CHAPTER 10

IBM 601 Automatic Multiplier (1941)
Courtesy of IBM Corporation.

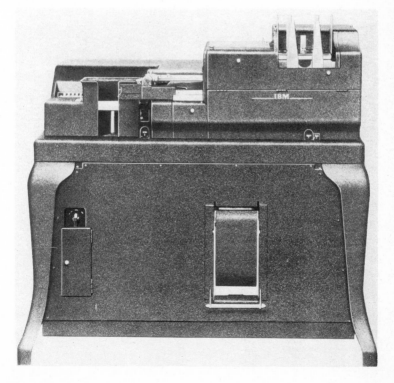

10

Real Time, Feedback, and Stability

REAL TIME   10.1

The expression *real time* is sufficiently peculiar to require some explanation, particularly because there are two distinct meanings. The first meaning arose from simulation problems. Many simulation problems done on a computer involve time, but the time referred to in the simulation bears little or no relation to elapsed time on a clock. Thus in this type of problem there are two times. It is necessary to refer both to the time in the problem and to the computing time used by the machine, and the latter is called real time to distinguish it from the fictitious time in the problem. Frequently the times are more or less proportional to each other. But, on a problem like a moon shot, the flight time along the trajectory at launch time may run somewhat slower than elapsed machine time, but in midflight it is usually the other way around, and hours of flight time require only a few minutes of machine time.

There is now a second meaning to real time. In many problems there is an interaction between the machine and the real world, and it is necessary for the machine to respond in real time if the results are to be used in the real world. Thus the computer that guides the takeoff of a moon shot *must* supply guidance instructions at the proper times. The computer cannot take too much time to calculate the next instruction because then the results would be available too late to be used. If the computer must give a new set of guidance instructions every 1/10 of a second, then the computer must complete its computations in less than 1/10 of a second. It is probably this second meaning of real time that is referred to these days when you hear of real time.

As a simple example of real-time application, we once used a small computer to gather data from a cyclotron (later from a Van de Graaff). The data came from *randomly* occurring nuclear disintegrations. It was necessary for the machine first to recognize that an event had occurred and then to take in and store the corresponding data. In order to recognize an event the designers equipped the machine with several *real-time interrupts*.

The idea of a real-time interrupt is central to real-time computing (in the second sense). An interrupt is a signal from the world external to the computer to its internal world (of constantly following out instructions of a program, one after another).

One way of accomplishing this interruption of its normal path of computation is to place in the current address register an address that sends the control to a location where the proper special program has been stored. Suppose this is the program to read the appropriate data from some external device and to store the data in the proper place. The interrupt must also store in a standard place the address that was in the current address register so that when the special processing program is done the control can be transferred to the earlier task and it can be resumed.

Unfortunately, some of the operations of a computer, such as a division, may require so much time to be completed that the external world cannot be kept waiting that long. To meet this requirement the real-time interrupt often halts the currently running program at some suitable substep of the operation being done, stores information about the current status of *all* the necessary components of the machine (including the current address register), and transfers the control to a special location.

A third way to implement an interrupt is to have what amounts to a second control unit independent of the first, with its own current address register that is set initially by the interrupt. The second control unit is often restricted to a limited class of simple instructions, none of which take much time to execute. When the interrupt occurs the machine is "frozen" at the next small step of internal machine time. This can halt long operations but cannot halt the limited class that the second control can use. When the interrupt completes its task the rest of the machine is "unfrozen," and the old problem is resumed where it left off.

In the application mentioned above, using a computer to gather data from an experiment on a cyclotron, a data display program was run when nothing else was urgent. When an interrupt signalled that a random nuclear event had occurred, the interrupt program halted the display and stored the data. After the data was safely stored the control was then normally transferred to a second program whose purpose was to process the data. If, however, the interrupt came from the data processing program, then the most recent data was put in a queue and the control went back to where it was, and the data being processed at the time the interrupt occurred was again taken up.

At the end of the data processing routine, an examination was made to see if any further data needed processing (as in the queue), and if so, the next item was processed.

When there was no more data to be processed, then the control went back to the program that displayed the processed data on an oscilloscope for human inspection. Thus there were essentially three programs:

1. a very short one to grab and store an event
2. a program to reduce the data
3. a program to display the data

They have the obvious corresponding priorities, with the first one having a queue so that, in emergencies due to two or more events coming too rapidly in succession, the program can still cope with them. The possibility of the first program getting interrupted by itself could not occur in this case because of the inherent delay (dead time) of the external recording equipment.

When a machine is asked to tend to a number of different things, interrupts may occur from one or more sources. The hardware of the machine usually has a built-in priority interrupt system so that the lower priority programs can be interrupted by the higher priority ones but not vice versa. The number of levels depends, of course, on the number of distinct sources of interrupts that are connected to the machine.

Process Control Computers

The example of recording nuclear data that we gave illustrates the use of the machine to accept and process data from the real world, but not to react back on the real world. Far more interesting are those problems like trajectory guidance in which the results from the real world are processed and then used to affect the real world again. Such a program monitors the flight, especially the takeoff, and from the numbers it gets, the program calculates the next set of steering instructions to be used. This requires the computing to be done at a rapid rate so that the trajectory corrections can be applied before it is too late. For such applications real-time computers must have fast internal speeds.

When the machine is permanently used to monitor or control some piece of equipment in the real world, say, a chemical plant, then it is sometimes called a *process control computer*. Such computers must be extremely reliable because frequent failures would ruin the external equipment they are controlling. Indeed, the problem is to make the system *fail-safe*, so that when the inevitable failure occurs everything is not ruined. This is a nontrivial problem, but there is a good deal of experience to guide the programmer in preparing his *fail-safe* program. One widely used solution is to use a pair of computers in parallel, with one doing the actual controlling while the second computer monitors the first. In the event of a disagreement between the two computers a short program is run to try to determine which of the two is faulty and take it out of the system, leaving the other to operate the system alone. Of course, a diagnostic is also printed out for humans to read which indicates where the trouble is probably located and alerts the repairmen. Encoding information inside a general-purpose computer in an error-detecting code is the most commonly used method for catching the single errors. So far, only a few large general-purpose computers have used error-correcting code representation internally for correcting isolated malfunctions so that the computation can go on while the repairman fixes the machine. It is important to note that not only do

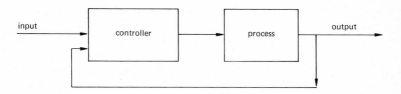

Figure 10-1 A feedback system.

such codes catch errors, they also tend to pinpoint the failing part, thus making maintenance much easier.

Most process control computers have analog-to-digital converters to go from the analog variables measured to the numbers needed by the machine, and, at the output, digital-to-analog converters to set the values of the apparatus it is controlling.

FEEDBACK 10.2

Feedback is almost a self-descriptive word. In the abstract it takes the form shown in the diagram (Figure 10-1) with a detecting device, or input, feeding into the controller. Part of the output is also fed back into the controller. The controller compares the input with the output signal, and, based on the difference between them, sends instructions to the process to alter itself appropriately.

A simple specific example of feedback is driving a car down a straight highway. The process is the actual steering to stay on the road, and the controller is the part of the brain that compares where the car appears to be with where it is supposed to be and then sends signals to alter the position of the steering wheel. The power of the feedback system is clear. Even though there may be random small bumps in the highway and the wind blows the car this way and that, the simple feedback system keeps the car going almost straight down the road. Indeed, feedback also compensates for the fact that we cannot originally set the wheel so that the car will go right down the middle of the road even when there are no small random disturbances. Thus it also handles the fact that we cannot determine precisely what the initial (starting) conditions are.

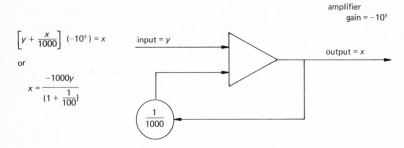

Figure 10-2   A feedback amplifier.

Another simple example is the classic feedback amplifier circuit. The amplifier itself is built to have a large *gain*, that is, the input voltage is amplified, say, about 100,000 times but with the output having the opposite sign to the input. In practice, because of initial variations and aging of the components, the actual gain will vary with time, as well as from amplifier to amplifier as they come off the production line. But by taking, say, 1/1000 of the output and feeding it back to the input, we get a feedback amplifier with a gain of about 1000, which is not very sensitive to the gain of the original amplifier. The simple equations are shown in Figure 10-2.

Here we have given up a lot of the possible gain to get a controlled gain that is almost independent of the amplification (the 1/100 factor in the denominator). The accuracy of the gain depends mainly on the resistor that takes 1/1000 of the output and returns it to the input.

It is widely believed that the human system uses feedback in many different ways. It is claimed that when you reach for a glass of water you start a motion, then sense how far you have gone, and use the remaining distance as a signal for further action. Thus you continually correct yourself and "home in" on the goal.

Variations on the feedback device are numerous and the applications are widespread. The power of the feedback approach lies in the fact that we do not set out to do the job exactly right the first time, but merely move in the right direction to reduce the error. We monitor the difference between the input signal (in the glass of water case, the input signal is to reduce the distance between the glass and the hand to zero) and the output (our hand's position) to control the subsequent actions. Similarly, a chemical plant may be set to operate at a given temperature, and the difference between the actual and the desired temperatures is used to increase or decrease the heat put into the system. Home temperature regulation is much the same.

Machine Applications

The application of the feedback principle to computers occurs at many levels. Often the designers have used it in the internal operation of the machine itself, both in individual circuits and in bigger units. When the computer is used in a process control situation, it usually operates in a feedback situation that monitors the behavior of the system, compares it with the desired behavior, and makes suitable adjustments to reduce the observed differences.

Being a very flexible device, the computer may be used in subtle ways. Thus, in a space shot, there is an initially desired trajectory for the missile. When the launching occurs, the actual behavior of the missile is measured and compared with the desired, and when the inevitable differences are observed, orders are sent out to change various guidance parts, such as the fin settings. But the computer *does not* try to get it back on the original trajectory. Rather, it tries to get it onto one which will end with the same conditions without having the trajectories coincide all along the way.

The midcourse corrections that are usually reported in the news of the space shots to the moon and the planets on television programs are examples of feedback and show the basic problems fairly clearly. Although the launch may have gone as accurately as possible, the passage of time reveals small differences that gradually grow into big differences. If we wait long enough the small errors in velocity or initial angle will result in large errors in position. Thus, the longer we wait, the more accurately we can estimate the errors we made and hence the *miss distance* that will occur. But, the longer we wait, the more energy (fuel) we will have to expend to get the missile back into a suitable orbit.

Experience seems to have arrived at the compromise of correcting at about the middle of the trajectory if things go right. But, in difficult situations with large errors and limited fuel, the correction must be made when there is still enough fuel to do the job—which may be a good deal sooner than originally planned.

Let us repeat the point: simple feedback systems try to bring the system back to the planned path (signal, temperature, or whatever is desired) as soon as possible, but more sophisticated uses, which usually involve a computer, try to alter the situation so that the final result will be what is desired without following the original plan all the way.

STABILITY   10.5

While we have described the usual feedback situation, we have at the same time glossed over some serious problems. The complete theory of feedback is highly mathematical and cannot be covered here. We can only give some typical troubles that arise in practice and indicate in a general way what must be done to handle these difficulties.

In the example of the person driving the car, a beginner is apt to suddenly notice that the car is drifting to one side of the road and respond by making a large correction to the wheel. The result is that very soon he finds that the car is now approaching the other side even more rapidly. This is an example of the effect of making too large a response to the error signal—overreacting, it is often called.

Another example is typified by the person in a shower trying to adjust the temperature to suit himself. Especially in the older showers there is a large water capacity in the pipe leading from the place where the water is controlled to the nozzle where the water comes out. As a result the following sequence of events is likely to happen. First, being somewhat too cold, the person turns the hot water knob up a bit. After a few moments since he still does not feel that the water is getting warmer, he turns it up some more. He still does not detect the water warming up, so he turns it up still more! Finally the water begins to warm up and he is satisfied—but it contines to get hotter, so he starts to turn it down a bit. But it continues to get still hotter and he is forced to turn the hot down a lot, lest he get burned. Soon the water will be too cold, and the cycle gets going again and he again turns the hot water up. In this case it is clear that it is the *time delay* between the taking of the action and the result being available for measurement that produces the tendency to overreact. Thus the *delay* in the system is an important feature of a feedback control system. The effect of too much delay is to produce instability in the form of "hunting" for the right value, with the swings growing in amplitude as time goes on.

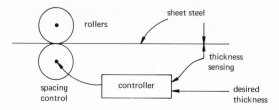

Figure 10-3 Schematic of a rolling mill.

Some human diseases, such as certain muscle spasms, are believed to be due to instability of the feedback system, and drugs are sometimes used to control the magnitude of the response system so that the human does not break into oscillation about the intended result. One occasionally observes people who have these troubles. Such afflicted persons often try to cope with the situation by *not* trying at the last minute, thus cutting out the feedback loop and coasting to the goal.

When the computer is used in a process control situation these same effects can arise. In a steel mill, where the computer gets information about the thickness of the sheet steel coming out of the rollers in order to maintain a given thickness, the delay from the setting of the rollers to the sensing of the resulting thickness of the sheet steel some distance away from the mill rollers will give rise to instability and an oscillation unless this effect is understood and allowed for in the computer program. Here again we have the classic conflict of interest: the sooner we get the rollers back to what we think is the right spacing, the sooner the plate being rolled will be the proper size, but too rapid and too large a response will result in overshooting (overreacting) and further adjustments in the opposite direction. A properly designed feedback system tries to get rapid correction without overshooting and the consequent hunting for the desired value.

Hunting for the correct value is a clear symptom of a fault in the feedback design. Hunting involves the great risk that as time goes on, the oscillations will inevitably grow in amplitude until the mechanism destroys itself.

The guided missile provides an interesting example of the feedback problems that can arise. In the early part of the flight, the feedback from the predicted target position and the predicted missile position is used to slowly bring the missile back into an interception path. But as the "time to go" to interception decreases, it is necessary to respond more and more rapidly (and violently) to the observed and predicted miss distances. Thus the feedback system has a changing amount of feedback that gradually approaches the dangerous overshoot condition and reaches instability only at the moment of impact (we hope).

Although feedback was used in many ways by the ancient Romans, it was mainly during and after the Second World War that feedback became a separate science. While feedback can be used in purely mechanical situations, most applications use electronic systems, and it is the widespread availability of reliable, flexible electronic amplifiers and other electronic information processing units that has made the feedback control field expand until it is the heart of most of our better, more complex control systems.

The computer, by its ability to compute complicated expressions rapidly and to make complicated choices, has given a new impetus to the field by greatly increasing the range of application and the quality of the results obtained. Thus the computer is often the vital part of a complicated control system, and it can be expected to become even more common as the years go on and the problems become more complex while performance is expected to improve. We have only sketched the briefest aspects of the problem, and for those interested we recommend a standard text in feedback and control.

The computer is often used to simulate a proposed feedback control system and to study its behavior in order to find good ways of designing the final system. Later a computer can be used as the control element.

Because computers are so useful in control situations and are so widely used in new control applications, the Computer Revolution is often called the Control Revolution. The Industrial Revolution gave us the *power* to do things. The Computer Revolution is giving us the *control* over the use of this power.

CONTROL OF EXPERIMENTS   10.4

In Chapter 9, "The Computer As an Experimental Tool," we mentioned briefly the use of computers to control experiments. At first computers were used to gather data, and on the basis of the analysis of the data by the computer, the computer altered the experiment being done. A good example of this is the atomic pile. Just as the pile is about to cool off, the external control raises the control rods and lets the pile heat up. Just as the pile is about to blow up, the control lowers the control rods to absorb neutrons and cool the pile. Thus the computer, operating in micro- to milliseconds keeps the atomic pile at a critical level. Experiments like keeping an atomic pile at a given temperature require the balancing of large opposing forces very precisely, and therefore such experiments present the possibility of the very precise measurement of something. Such experiments are, of course, dangerous because of the possibility of an explosion and should be approached with caution. Their potential has hardly been explored and we can expect to see many more of them in the coming years—some with disastrous results, too! The understanding of the stability of the feedback loops is clearly of vital importance before embarking on such experiments. The fail-safe aspects must also be studied carefully.

In experimenting with animals it is sometimes convenient to couple the animal into a loop with a machine so that the machine controls the stimuli that are presented to the animal. Thus the stimuli can be made to be contingent in complex ways upon past responses. Again, the speed and reliability of the machine make it much superior to humans trying to do the same job.

Experiments which use the computer as the control element of the experiment are rapidly increasing in number. The direct control of a production line, or some other rather rigid process, is economically important, but it is the use of the computer as a controller with a widely varying range of possible responses that has the intellectual challenge. In a way we can regard the topic of artificial intelligence (Chapter 14) as being a study of how to program a machine to respond to a wide range of situations without ourselves having to analyze all the possible combinations that may arise. Thus in a chess-playing routine, the planner of the program simply cannot imagine every possible board position that the program might face and then provide for each possibility. Rather, he tries to give some broad strategy to cope with all possible board positions.

Types of Control

The earliest control theory of any generality (which occurred much later than the earliest practice) was the so-called linear, or proportional, control, in which the correction signal is proportional (in size) to the error signal. Thus large errors produce large corrections, while small errors produce small corrections. In such a system it is comparatively easy to analyze the situation to determine the stability. Because it was easily understood it tended to be widely used, and it was often claimed to be "optimal" (usually without carefully specifying what optimal meant).

Common sense suggests that for really effective control, the immediate use of all the resources you have to correct the observed error would keep one closest to the desired value. Such systems are often called *bang-bang* because we are "banging" against either one limit of our ability to correct or else against the other limit. We are always forcing the system as hard as it can go. The theory for such systems is much more complex than the theory for linear systems, but often the actual realization in hardware is easier.

Consider the well-known example of bang-bang control occurring in the common hot air house furnace system (see Figure 10-4). The oil burner is either on full or it is off; it is *not* proportional to the temperature difference between the room and the desired temperature. This is sensible design because for efficient heating the burner should operate with a given flame size.

The blower fan is likewise either on or off. It goes on if and only if the heat exchanger has a temperature above a set minimum (180° in our figure).

The oil burner is on only if two conditions are both met: the room is too cool and the heat exchanger is not too hot.

In this bang-bang system (it uses relays) the temperature control is achieved by the *length of time* the heating is applied and not by the intensity of the heat. This is characteristic of bang-bang systems: the duration of the full signal is the means of control, not the intensity, as it is in proportional control.

This example has no stability problem. There could be one if at the same time there were equipment for cooling which was activated whenever the room was too hot. With both heating and cooling it is easy to see how the instability could arise, but it is harder to analyze precisely how to control it in a sensible fashion.

Similarly, in space shots we do not try to control the rate at which the propulsion engines work. Instead, we control the duration of burning—typical of modern bang-bang control.

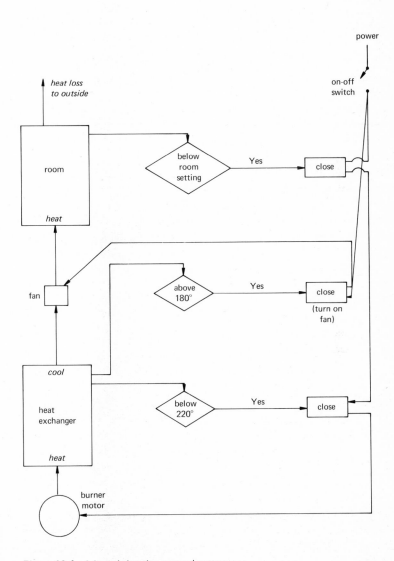

Figure 10-4 A hot-air heating control system.

OVERLOAD AND FAIL-SAFE   10.5

In the furnace example we see one elegant solution to the overload problem: when the heat exchanger gets too hot the burner is simply turned off, and we *fail-safe*.

The problem of fail-safe is very complex but is obviously of fundamental importance to complex situations. Many computers have a fail-safe feature in case of power failure—at least for the main memory. This is simply a special circuit that senses a drop in the regulated output of the computer power supply. As soon as the drop is noted the computer automatically stops its normal processing and stores all its volatile information. Since the power regulator normally has enough power to operate at least 1/1000 of a second beyond the point where the power failure can be detected, there are, therefore, more than 1000 microseconds available for the storage process. Heavy power consuming units like tape drivers are often not so protected, but by suitable programming the system can weather power failures gracefully.

But, in the general process control situation, fail-safe is essentially difficult to achieve. Each case must be separately analyzed.

Similarly, in a corporation's accounting and record keeping system careful planning can ensure that an isolated loss of computer power (due perhaps to a machine breakdown) does not bring the whole system to a crashing halt with the resulting chaos. With proper planning the computing capacity that still exists can be used to keep the vital parts going—much as the human system cuts back its operation (perhaps to the extent of losing consciousness) as it reaches overload but tries to preserve the vital functions as long as it can. When the overload condition passes, the system is brought back into operation in a safe sequence. Unfortunately, fail-safe and orderly recovery are rarely planned for by the data processing department, and as a result the user is regularly exposed to periods of chaos. Presumably, time and experience will teach the planners to consider such matters.

SUMMARY   10.6

The use of the computer as a control device in the real world requires it to react in real time. This introduces the concepts of *feedback* and its concomitant problem of *stability*. Unless some care is taken, a feedback system will not control a process properly. Instead, it will break into violent oscillations and likely destroy the equipment it is supposed to control.

There are many types of control, and the computer with its great power and flexibility has enabled us to use much more sophisticated control systems than we could before it was available. Its use, however, raises questions of *reliability* and *fail-safe* when failures do occur. While fail-safe has been recognized in physical plants, it is not often clearly recognized in accounting, business, and other digital applications.

Mark I Relay Computer (1944)
Courtesy of IBM Corporation.

11

Language and Information Retrieval

EVOLUTION OF COMPUTER LANGUAGES 11.1

We propose to first review briefly the evolution of computer languages. It should now be clear that the computer uses sequences of binary digits both as the basis for its processes (its operations and the addresses of its operands) and for the information that it operates upon (numbers, letters, or whatever meaning the user has given to the sequences of 0s and 1s). There are a few machines which appear to the user to operate in the decimal notation, but we will ignore them for the moment.

In the earliest stages of the evolution of computers it was necessary to give directly to the machine the proper sequences of 0s and 1s for the particular problem at hand. This, as we have repeatedly observed, is difficult for humans to do. Probably the first general-purpose programs to be written were routines for conversion from decimal to binary and back again. These were called *subroutines* and were called into use in the machine by appropriately

1. specifying where the data to be operated upon was,
2. specifying where the control was to return to when the subroutine was done,
3. then transferring control to the subroutine.

When control came to the subroutine the subroutine carried out its function and then returned control to the main program at the place specified in (2).

Routines for handling input and output were similarly designed and handled as subroutines. Even this small step forward in the ease of use of machines was recognized as a change in the language of communication. Instead of writing all the individual instructions for some process, a fixed pattern of operations (the subroutine) was called into use by a short, standard sequence of instructions (steps 1-3 above).

Another advance was the realization that we can write mnemonic symbols such as ADD for the operations (much as we have done in the text) instead of the 0s and 1s that the machine uses, and that the machine itself can, using a table lookup, find the appropriate sequence of 0s and 1s to write (during loading of the program into storage) in place of the symbols we wrote. From these symbolic operations we evolved a few *pseudo-operations* (now often called *macros*) that were not in the instruction repertoire of the machine, but which the input loading routine could easily recognize. It could then write a moderately long sequence of instructions corresponding to the pseudo-operation, rather than a single instruction at a time.

Shortly after we started using mnemonic symbols for the operations we realized we could use symbolic names for the operands and let the machine assign definite addresses where the quantities were to be stored. It could later substitute these binary addresses into the program whenever the corresponding symbolic name occurred. Again, this substitution occurs at the time the program is loaded into the machine.

The combination of symbolic names for operations and addresses plus a few pseudo-operations was a significant step forward. The program that performs this process is given the name *assembler*. The language of communication was by this means much more suitable for human use than were the original binary instructions and addresses that the engineer designed into the machine. But it should be clearly realized that the machine still obeys only sequences of 0s and 1s and operates on them. It does not and cannot at present use directly the symbolic language that the program is written in. An *assembler program* (operating in machine language) is needed to translate from the language we write to the language the machine uses when it executes the program.

The trivial example of an interpreter given in Chapter 4 should indicate how an assembler operates. The difference is that the interpreter creates the machine instructions and uses them, while a compiler creates the instructions and stores them for use after the entire program has been translated.

The essential steps that the assembler program must do to convert the program written by the human into machine language are these:

1. Scan the input to recognize what is coming in.
2. For each symbolic instruction, do a simple table lookup to replace the bit pattern of the letters of the operation by the appropriate bit pattern for the corresponding machine operation.
3. For each symbolic instruction, see if the bit pattern of the address of the operand is in the operand address table, and

    a. if so, fill in the corresponding address in binary form.

    b. if not, assign to the operand address the next available address in storage *and* enter both the name and the location in the operand table.
4. For pseudo-operations, find the appropriate set of instructions and write them down.
5. Recognize other "meta-language" inputs such as

    a. comments the author used, which are to be ignored.

    b. END and similar instructions that tell the assembler what to do to the program as a whole.
6. For transfer of control instructions, make another table of addresses of where the labeled instructions occur (translated of course). This table must be used to later fill in forward references in the program to places that the assembler has not yet reached.

Even without any further details, the reader can now probably come close to simulating an assembler by following the above pattern of operations. In an actual assembler there are, of course, many details that we have omitted as well as frills and conveniences that are necessary for practical use.

Many pseudo-operations produce from one line of written code much more than one line of machine code. However, the assembler mainly translates line for line from the symbolic language to the machine language. It was promptly recognized that what is really wanted is to have a few instructions written by the human produce a large number of machine instructions. Otherwise the human would find that he was spending too much of his time writing out long lists of instructions for a given program. A number of different languages have been developed to meet this requirement, and while there has been a lot of talk about a *universal language* for doing all problems, what we have produced are mainly special purpose languages. Probably the most famous language is FORTRAN, whose form is close to typical mathematical formulas and which translates from this language into machine language. The COBOL language is designed to do much the same for business problems.

But so far no completely satisfactory languages have been found, and the search goes on trying to match the best features of human languages to those of machines.

NATURAL LANGUAGE TRANSLATION   11.2

Early in the history of machine computation there arose the idea of having a machine translate from one natural language (in this country, usually from Russian) into another (usually English). At the earliest talking stages, there emerged two definite schools of thought, those who believed, "Of course machines can do the job, once sufficiently large vocabularies are provided in the storage of the machine," and those who thought, "Machines will never be able to do translations from one natural language to another."

The results appear (to this author) to be a draw. Far more was accomplished than the opponents thought could be done, but (while there is still some quibbling) apparently no generally successful machine translations have been produced over a reasonably wide range of subject matter. This is at least the gist of the recent Pierce report to the government.

It was soon apparent that if success were to be easy, then for N languages we would need something like $N(N - 1)/2$ translating programs to go from any one to any other. Thus there arose the beguiling idea of a single central language, probably different from any existing natural language, to which and from which all translation could be done. This flourished briefly in spite of generations of philosophers who had grappled with the problem of "meaning" in language and had been unable to come up with anything significant. Needless to say, this grandiose approach has been quietly dropped, although some people still wishfully think it can be done in the near future.

THE NEW LINGUISTICS 11.3

Early in the evolution of artificial languages for use on machines we realized that we were trying to create languages for humans to use. Such natural languages as English, Russian, and German are the result of long evolution, are presumably well adapted to their function, and should therefore (so the argument goes) provide models for building synthetic languages. True, we do not want human to human communication, we want human to machine *and* back. The same language need not be used in both directions, though there are some obvious advantages in doing so.

For these reasons and others the people who were creating synthetic languages turned to classical linguistics with questions like "What is the engineering efficiency of having many synonyms in our natural language?", "What is the economic advantage of irregular verbs?", "What density of synonyms and antonyms should a language have?", and "Why is language ambiguous and is this a virtue or a necessary vice?".

If we are to *engineer* a language for humans to communicate with machines, presumably it will have some of the features of the natural languages and some of the features of machine languages. We therefore need to understand a great deal more than we do now about the engineering efficiencies of natural languages and how they fit the human nervous system. Along these lines there has been some research in how sentences can be created by a mechanical process and how a language may be written so that at least the parts of speech can be recognized by a simple process such as a machine can carry out. Research in these directions is being actively pursued.

The fact is that we have already had a good deal of experience with artificial languages in actual use, and we have begun to form some hypotheses about the questions and answers in this new type of linguistics. And, as we have observed before, when the questions are new, the answers are often new and interesting. Thus the presence of machines have helped to stimulate the creation of a relatively new field of research.

NEED FOR INFORMATION RETRIEVAL
AND SOME DIFFICULTIES   11.4

There is little doubt that there has been a "paper explosion" in recent years and that the current rapid growth is likely to continue for some time. This paper explosion is often identified as an information explosion, and it is claimed that information is growing exponentially (Chapter 2)—meaning that the amount of information available is doubling at fixed intervals of time (usually estimated at around 10 years).

One consequence of the information explosion is that often what one person is working on is already known to others and may even be readily available in the literature. This worries many people, especially congressmen making appropriations for research and development. It also bothers the individual worker in his day-to-day activities, since he justly fears that what he is working on is already well-known.

Because of this situation there are a great many papers and articles on the topic of the information explosion and the "unnecessary duplication of effort." It is fashionable to write about the problem and to say that computing machines will (somehow, magically) cure the problem if only enough money is appropriated to develop some system or other of information retrieval. I have found it convenient to judge such papers by the ratio of amount of effort they put on saying how important the problem is to how little they say in specific detail on how to do it. The more they stress the importance of the problem, the more it is likely that they have nothing to offer. It is not as if there have not been generations of librarians, from the days of the Library of Alexandria to the present, who have worried and thought about the problem of the storage and retrieval of information. If there were easy solutions, it is not likely they would have escaped centuries of searching. The belief that computing machines, being new, will permit new solutions is of course conceivable. This is the hope that so many people have. But important as the problem may be, there is much wishful thinking in most of the proposed solutions.

One of the major difficulties of research in this area is the utter confusion about how information is actually retrieved by real humans. The models formed are often based on a small, carefully selected field of work and its information retrieval needs, or even on sheer fantasy. A careful examination of actual methods that people use in retrieving information during a "library search" reveals many differing ways and needs, and it seems unlikely that we will find a single solution to all of the various requirements.

On the other hand, there is no doubt that specific systems of information retrieval operating for reasonable lengths of time have been valuable. What is open to question is whether a broad system covering wide areas of knowledge and operating over long periods of time will be effective. These qualifying remarks are important. It appears that, systematic classifiers to the contrary, knowledge in various fields is currently organized in very different ways. Indeed, often the greatest contribution to a field is not the discovery of new knowledge, but the discovery of a new way of organizing what is already known. Even a single field of knowledge does not always have a unique structure for its information.

The limitation to reasonable lengths of time is a result of the observation that the kind of question asked in a field, as well as the subject matter of the field, tends to change as time goes on. Consider, for example, the earlier part of this chapter where we raised the problem of the new, engineering approach to linguistics. The engineering questions now being asked are foreign to the older classical way of looking at the field of linguistics, and one strongly suspects that an information system (even an "open-ended" one) designed in the earlier years to handle classical linguistics would be completely unable to cope with the new class of questions.

In this connection it is interesting to search, say, 20 years of *Science Abstracts* for papers on a given subject and see how the headings under which it is listed change as one goes back in time.

We have given some of the difficulties in the field of information retrieval for science and research, and even for engineering. First, it is a subject that has been examined closely for many years, so it is well worked over. Second, the way information is actually retrieved by humans at present is not well understood: inaccurate and misleading models are proposed and solutions for these models are offered. Third, actual experimentation is expensive and hard to do. The working habits of scientists and others who depend on information are often personal, and such people are not willing to experiment much, having always the need to get on with their own work. The promise of help from the modern computer should not be overlooked, though this author believes that too much is expected from it. One leading worker in the field, disgusted with proposed systems, said that in view of the work already done, any new proposals before being taken seriously, should be forced to produce solid evidence as to why they would work. Too often, half-baked ideas are sponsored and large sums of money appropriated simply because the offered method seems to be plausible.

Indeed, if there were any short characterization of the field of information retrieval, it would be the almost total lack of fundamentally new ideas and the great tendency to grab a plausible amalgam of old ideas and hope that it, together with a machine, will provide an economically feasible system.

But let us observe, in spite of this strongly negative viewpoint, that there are many modest information retrieval systems that pay their way. It is the large, grandiose systems that are to solve *all* our problems *forever* that, I suspect, are constructed of wishful thinking.

A recommended procedure for entering the field is to watch yourself as you go about doing odd jobs of information retrieval in the course of a year. Note how indirectly so many of them operate, how flimsy was the initial information and how wrong was your starting point. As a trivial example, in trying to recover a person's name you are apt to say, "It begins with a *P*." With some suggestions like Phillip, Phillipson, etc., you come upon the ending *stone*. This suggests other associations and when the name is finally recovered (Johnstone), you see that none of the starting clues were actually correct!

Factual Information

We have been talking about information retrieval at what might be called "the idea level." There is also the information retrieval problem on the "factual level." "Mr. X (social security number Y) at address Z paid an income tax of Q dollars last year" is a typical fact. In this area problems are more manageable and there are a number of known ways of organizing the material so that the cost of retrieval is reasonably near minimal.

The problems in this field center around efficiency of operation, updating, correcting errors, handling special cases, gathering the original information, getting it into machine readable form, and so on. These are nontrivial because such data files tend to become large and the total operation expensive.

Between the "factual files" and "idea files" are tables like those of physical constants. Here the content appears to be factual information, but who is to decide which of the reported values in the literature is to be used? How is the table to be kept up to date? And if it is changed, how is the user to know that the value he used last week in preparing a report has been changed so that when others repeat his computations they will come up with a different answer? These are all awkward questions which require practical answers before embarking on such a *data bank*. (See Chapter 13.)

There is also the question of the completeness of the data file. Should there be a systematic effort made (and if so, by whom) to cover a definite class of data? A file that has occasional gaps can be very irritating to use. It always seems that what you want is missing. On the other hand, completeness tends to produce numerous entries in the table that are never used.

Large Data Bases

Closely associated with information retrieval is the idea of building up and keeping central files of factual information. For instance, cities keep files on the physical, social, and economic structure of the city in detail down to the individual buildings in the city. When these are in a computer and appropriate programs have been written, the city managers can study various plans for changes, such as slum clearance, welfare aid, and highway construction. The large data files in a machine mean potentially better planning, for the consequences of a plan can be more readily seen and alternatives more cheaply found. City and state unified crime statistics is another area in which large data bases are often used.

Occasionally mentioned is a central data base for the whole country that would cover all needs for planning. The advocates of such a system are fond of citing the needless duplication of present record keeping systems, the inefficiencies that occur because what one branch of some public organization has is needed but not available to another branch. In fact, they often understate the duplication and the losses due to the unavailability of information to those who need it.

The proponents of the central data file usually do not spell out in detail exactly what kinds of information will be kept and how, and to whom they will and will not be available, since they are still in the planning stages. It is probably this very vagueness that so alarms the average person who immediately senses Big Brother, straight out of *1984. The Naked Society* by Vance Packard dramatizes some of this.

There is a classic conflict of interest here. On the one hand there are the clear savings in effort that would result from a centrally controlled data system. There are also the great new possibilities that would come from having complete details on all aspects of our society so that we could study and plan reliably. On the other hand, there is great fear of the misuse of the information, of the invasion of the privacy of the individual. (See Chapter 13 for more on this topic.)

The Idea of a Large Central Data Base

There is a good deal of talk and misconception about the popular idea of a central data base kept by the government. We would like to bring out a number of aspects of the problem that are often overlooked.

The intellectually inclined person is apt to assume that all knowledge is good—or at least that knowledge is preferable to ignorance—and then argue from this unstated assumption. A theme of a number of Greek tragedies as well as more recent literature is the undesirableness of knowing when, where, and how one is going to die. A few persons—criminals condemned to death and very sick people in a hospital, for example—have this knowledge fairly accurately, but most of us would rather not know. On the other hand, we do have and use the knowledge of the *average* behavior of people with regard to dying in the form of mortality tables, as well as from common observation. The aggregated knowledge is regarded as a good thing to have, but the specific knowledge about the individual is not.

Using the socially acceptable and socially unacceptable as a clue to what is and is not proper knowledge to have easily available, one may safely say to a group of friends that a certain percentage of their spouses have been unfaithful and the speaker will not be regarded as a social outcast. But to go on to say which ones, when, where, and with whom, would not be socially acceptable. From this it is a reasonable guess that such knowledge is suitable in the aggregate but not when given in specific detail.

Many other examples can be found where it is probably regarded as undesirable to know in detail but it is proper to know in the aggregated form. Thus it is not wise to argue that all knowledge is good *ipso facto* and that anyone who proposes to limit the kind of knowledge that is in a central data file is antiintellectual.

Secondly, most people have a desire for some privacy. For example, some will pay extra to have an unlisted phone number. But personal privacy is something like military security. One cannot be sure of keeping any particular piece of information secret from a determined opponent, but one can arrange things so that it is so hard to get each piece that the opponent has not the power (in money or effort) to find out everything. The central data bank removes this defense that the average person, perhaps unwittingly, uses to preserve his privacy. The claim that one should have nothing to hide does not mean that everyone wants his every act discussed publicly.

Those in favor of the central data bank claim that only authorized persons will have access, and they show how it can in principle be kept from others. But the prudent person worries about how easy it will be for someone to become an authorized person, and how fraud and careless slips will allow unauthorized persons to have access to the data.

A third big worry is that the data file will gradually build up a lot of false as well as accurate information, and that the individual will not have any practical way of defending himself against inaccurate contents.

While these points by no means exhaust the classes of fears, let us turn to the other side and look at some of the proposed advantages.

Much of the proposed knowledge could be used to operate our society more efficiently. As was remarked in the opening chapters, we live in a world dominated by information, and it is getting more so every year. The lack of accurate data upon which to base plans is very expensive to society. For example, one can imagine that, for the average individual, more complete data would result in better and more satisfactory placement in jobs, or at least alert him to more suitable job opportunities. Of course, there will be mistakes in both categories, but it is reasonable to suppose that the mistakes made in the presence of probable knowledge, will, on the average, be less than those made by operating in the dark. It is not proposed that the use of a central data file will produce perfection. It is only claimed that the central data file can hardly be worse than what we have now.

A second point often made by the proponents is the economic savings that would result. For society as a whole there would be much less record handling and keeping and updating. To the individual it *could* (not necessarily would) mean the end of filling out forms every time he wants to do something new or unusual: simply using his social security number could produce the details of his address, his mother's maiden name, and the similar trivia so often requested and so often utterly irrelevant to the needs of the situation.

A third point is that we could make new studies in demography, health, medicine, crime, and human behavior, to name a few, that are not now possible, and from these studies new knowledge would emerge to the ultimate benefit of the individual.

People who oppose the data file often have the idea that it would mean that some people would never be able to get jobs once defects were revealed in their records. But let us be reasonable about this matter. While it is not exactly true, there would be approximately as many jobs with such a central file as without it. To imagine the worst, suppose that there is a complete file on everyone and a person running a large business wants to hire some people. When he checks upon the job applicants, he will find that practically everyone will have some blemish on his record. The employer will simply not be able to fill all his job openings with people against whom there is not some small objection. Thus to a first approximation, all that a central data file of great completeness (accurate or not) will do is to redistribute the jobs. And if someone who now has a job would under those conditions find that he could not get the job, then it is also true that someone who does not now have a job will get one. It is therefore necessary to ask what will be the net effect. Will or will not the central data files (if not too inaccurate) tend to favor the more worthy persons (without defining more worthy)? Again, it is not a question of the proposed system being always just and fair, but whether it will do a better job than we are now doing.

There is also a fear that unscrupulous politicians will use the data file for evil, often unstated, purposes. However, the claims that it would tend to increase blackmail, for example, are probably quite wrong. The reverse is more likely to be true since a person could hardly be blackmailed on information readily available.

The proposal that we solve some of the dilemmas posed in the opening paragraphs by permitting only certain kinds of information to exist in the aggregated form will meet stiff opposition. When we want to study trends in families on such subjects as infidelity, abortion, suicide, insanity, and the like, it is necessary to record the information in a form in which the name of the individual can be recovered so that he can be connected with the proper families.

There seems to be no simple solution. There is little doubt that the process of consolidating our information files is now going on at a rapid pace. Not only are large corporations doing it internally, but as mentioned before, various governmental agencies are gradually doing the same. What it is necessary to find out is how far people who understand the two sides of the argument are willing to go, and where, and to what forms are they prepared to say: "Stop, this is going too far. We prefer the inefficiencies and their attendant cost to the other less tangible losses that will happen." Thus it is necessary to get many people to carry on the debate so that when the time comes to vote for this or that small step toward central data files, they will act and vote in their own enlightened self-interest. There seems to be no other way of arriving at the proper action than the slow process of democracy at work. The questions should not be decided solely on immediate economic gains.

SUMMARY 11.5

As we noted early in the book, it is necessary to communicate with a computer in some mutually understood language, and not necessarily in the language that the designers built into the computer. This has led to a gradual evolution of the languages we use to communicate, and to the study of the nature of language in a more engineering and scientific manner than was customary before computers came on the scene.

Machines, by their power to handle information, have raised many questions concerning the storage and retrieval of information. This is sometimes referred to as having a large data base, or data bank. Data banks can vary from containing hard factual information (such as social security numbers), to apparently factual information (like the currently accepted velocity of light) and more controversial personnel records. It is the latter that have aroused so much discussion. We hope to have partially illuminated the discussion by observing that it is not a question of the data bank having perfectly accurate information and it being always used wisely, but rather, whether machines cannot improve the presently very inaccurate, often misused system.

IBM 603 Electronic Multiplier (1946)
Courtesy of IBM Corporation.

12

Decisions and Optimization

DECISIONS

Many applications of computing machines involve one or more decisions. In the widely televised election returns the computer produces decisions as to which candidates are *likely* to win. In medical applications a diagnosis is made. In guiding a missile decisions are made as to how much to tilt the fins and when to cut off the motor, and so on.

There are at least three types of decisions:

1. those in which we seem to know what to do
2. those which are frankly an informed guess
3. those based on probability

The guidance of a missile is mainly one of the first type because, **when** we have the input information correct and when we know what we want to have happen, it is then clear what to compute. The second type of decision occurs in playing games like chess and checkers where we can only give a "reasonable" set of rules, since we do not know exactly what move to make next in all cases. In the election prediction, and in some medical diagnoses, all we can do is make a statistical guess based on the type of information that has been collected, and this may involve a mixture of the three kinds of probability we discussed in Chapter 7.

What the Machine Does

Exactly what does the machine do when a decision is produced by the machine? Ultimately, it comes down to one of two possible types of machine operations. First, it may be a two-way branch instruction such as

a. if the number is positive, go to the indicated location for the next instruction, otherwise continue doing the instructions in sequence
b. if it is not positive, go to the indicated location, otherwise . . . .
c. if the number (perhaps a difference which has just been found) is zero, go to . . . .

There are many other variants on the two-way branch type of instruction, but they all have the following form: the next instruction is found either at the address indicated in the instruction or else it is the next instruction, the choice of which depends on some number just found. In all of these the branch is accomplished by the machine putting an address from the two-way branch instruction into the current address register.

Second, besides the two-way branch instructions, there is another type of branch instruction, the COMPUTED GO TO that operates as follows: an address is computed, either based entirely on internally generated numbers, or in part on some numbers that have been read in at some previous time, and this number is moved (either directly or indirectly) from the accumulator into the current address register. In this way we get a *many-way branch* based on a single computed number.

The two methods of altering the sequence of instructions being done differ mainly in emphasis in *how* the address is constructed. In the first method it *tends* to have been assigned by the programmer in advance, and represents a binary choice. In the second method it is a multiple choice based on a computed address. In a large program there are, of course, many branch points in the complete program, but all the branches are essentially one of the above two types.

Now it may be argued that this is all that humans do, or it may be argued that humans have other methods that are not equivalent to a sequence of simple choices (or elaborations of simple choices). In fact, not enough is known about how humans operate to substantiate one view or the other. What can be said is that we have found that many complicated situations can apparently be broken down into a sequence of simple decisions of the two types mentioned. Indeed, experience has produced many situations which people once thought were too complicated to be analyzed but which have now been broken down into these elementary decisions. But this does not say that *all* situations can be so broken down.

The situation is something like what happened in arithmetical problems. Experience over thousands of years has produced techniques of analyzing situations into sequences of simple additions, subtractions, multiplications, and divisions. However, we have so far found that not all problems that arise in life can be solved by arithmetic, though a surprisingly large number can. Similarly, close and careful analysis over many years has developed techniques for breaking many complex situations requiring decisions into sequences of simple decisions, while many situations remain that have not been so mastered.

The Simple Decision Situations

In many engineering and scientific applications, the decisions to be made can be based on definite information (or close to definite information), and the resulting actions to be taken are similarly rather definite in each case, although the details of the theory may be difficult and take years to master. Thus the action in a feedback control system, for example, is usually obvious for various situations. In the case of a steel mill rolling sheet steel, if the sheet coming out is found to be too thick, it is necessary to bring the rollers closer together, and if too thin, the rollers should be separated. The stability of the feedback loop must, of course, be considered in the final design.

Again, when calculating a trajectory to the moon it is necessary, among other things, to watch the distance from the missile to the center of the moon, and when this is less than the radius of the moon, then it is necessary to back up the computation a bit and compute the actual impact point. If it is a very accurate simulation of the landing, then data about the moon's surface in the neighborhood of the estimated impact point is needed to determine the local distance from the center to the surface, and some method of repeated trials may be used to get the needed numbers. Here we have the machine making a simple decision to switch from one program, for calculating the next step in the trajectory in free space, to another program, for finding the impact point, and the decision to switch programs is based on the distance of the calculated missile position from the surface of the moon.

When police monitor the license plates of cars crossing a bridge, they send the numbers to a computer, the computer searches a file of wanted plate numbers, and if it finds a match then the machine reports out the relevant information. If it does not find a match then it reports out NO MATCH— a simple matching and branching program.

When described in this way, there is nothing mysterious about machines making decisions. Indeed, *decision* seems a rather fancy name for a trivial process. But when the decisions are organized in a complex sequence, then rather sophisticated things can be built from a long sequence of simple single decisions. This effect is a consequence of the same "order of magnitude change" that was discussed at some length in Chapter 1. Tremendous repetition of simple steps seems to us to produce fundamental differences in effect.

Statistical Decisions

Many of the decisions that computers produce are based on statistics, and, for a close examination of what the computer does, it is necessary to have the technical background of statistics. We cannot teach a course in statistics here, but we can make reasonably clear the idea of what is going on.

It is a slight oversimplification, but one can say that the theory of probability is concerned with going from the probabilities of the individual events to the probabilities of compound events. The set of all possible elementary events is called the *population* or the *ensemble* of events. Probability theory uses the probabilities of the (simple) events in the basic population and estimates the probabilities of the compound (complex) events.

Statistics is the reverse process. We are given samples of the compound events and are asked to estimate the original underlying probabilities of the original population. To be specific, consider the election returns. Probability theory would enable you to estimate from the actual votes cast what you would observe if you took a sample. But the election return people wish to go the other way, to go from a specific sample of the election returns to a prediction of how the whole of the population will vote.

To make their estimate they first study the issues of the election and try to decide what are the relevant things to look for. (This involves some of the personal probabilities discussed before.) Then they carefully go over the past elections and try to find places in the East (which votes first) which seem to best indicate how the vote will depend on each particular issue. These are called *key areas*, and a strong attempt is made to get these returns of the voting into the computer as early and as accurately as possible. Then appropriate statistical tests are applied and an estimate is made as to the probable outcome.

One of the features of statistics is that it gives not certainty but only what is *hoped* to be the probabilities that their guess is accurate ("hoped" because the probabilities are based on assumptions about the underlying population that may or may not be accurate). So far the election predictors have been fairly lucky, but because they are pressed to make a guess as soon as they can (before the other networks do) and hence must jump to the result even though very little information is available, it is likely that sooner or later they will make some serious mistakes. It should be evident that election predictions use a mixture of both frequency and personal probabilities.

While some medical diagnoses may be definite in the sense that the given set of symptoms can only indicate one thing, usually it is a probability guess that the symptoms indicate such and such a situation. The probabilities come from experience with many cases and rest only partially on the frequency probability model. However, the situation in medicine allows an iterative process to be used. It is iterative in the sense that if there is doubt about which of a number of things the symptoms might indicate, then the computer being used in the diagnosis can print out a request for further examinations. Indeed, what is usually imagined is that the doctor will use the machine to help guide his examination, based in part on the medical record inside the machine, and in part on other data, such as current epidemic data, for example. The machine will not make the final decisions. Rather, it will print out that it might be one of several things (with associated probabilities opposite each diagnosis). There is much talk of someday connecting each doctor's machine into a nationwide net so that (1) his records are automatically entered into a common pool for studies of epidemics, and (2) indications of epidemics based on other doctors' data will in turn automatically alter the probabilities associated with various symptoms. From the combined records of all doctors it is generally supposed that valuable medical information can be found by other researchers.

We are probably very far in time from realizing such grandiose schemes because, if for no other reason, the awkward problem of legal responsibility will have to be solved before such a scheme can be widely used. When, due to an error, the patient dies, who will be responsible?

Some successes, in limited areas, have apparently been achieved, but we are still (1970) far from having automated medical information and diagnosis in this country, though one often reads in newspapers (but does not necessarily believe) of such medical predictions done in this country and elsewhere. Nor is it completely clear that this is what is wanted anyway. There are many doctors who regard some of their success in certain types of cases as being due mainly to the patient's faith in the doctor rather than to the treatment they prescribe, and they suspect that machines would not inspire the same degree of confidence (though some experts in computing complain that too much faith is now put in machine outputs).

Another example of statistical testing is that of studying authorship and the style of an author to find out who *might* have written something. This type of research is based on studying such things as word and sentence length distributions, types of punctuations used, the use of key words as *on* or *upon* in certain constructions. As in the election returns, one first tries to find some key items (analogous to the key areas in elections) to use as the basis for the test. Here the skill and knowledge of the expert is invaluable. Having chosen the things to try, then routine statistical tests will uncover how good these indicators are probably going to be, and the less effective ones can be eliminated. Then the actual unknown text can be run through and the results compared with the results from the various suspected authors. In this way the questions as to who wrote some of the Federalist papers, the different authorship of the Iliad and the Odyssey, and a recent elaborate study of some letters of unknown authorship in England were all (probably) settled. There have been similar studies of the authorship of various parts of the Bible, such as the (probable) multiple authorship of the book of Isaiah, and the books attributed to Moses.

PERT Charts

There are many applications of computers that require decisions. One of the simplest to understand, and one which does not involve

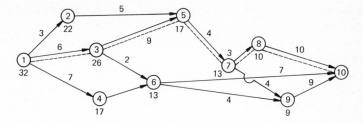

Figure 12-1 A PERT Chart. The dotted line shows the critical path, and the numbers below circles give the time before target date that the node must be reached.

elaborate statistics, is the so-called PERT chart, from P̲rogram E̲valuation R̲eview T̲echnique. (Sometimes it is called CPM chart from the name C̲ritical P̲ath M̲ethod.) PERT charts got their first great wave of publicity in connection with the Polaris submarine project. They were publicly credited with greatly speeding up the entire project, and it was completed many months ahead of schedule.

The central idea is quite simple to understand, though not always easy to carry out in practice. Let us take the submarine as an example. Making a submarine involves many parts and processes of assembly. The first step in the PERT process is to analyze carefully the processes involved in making the submarine and then to draw a chart showing, for each step, all other steps which must be done before it can be carried out. This chart is usually drawn as a complex graph (see Figure 12-1). The nodes represent points in time, and the processes are the lines between the nodes of the graph. Each node has branches running out of it to those processes which depend upon it and branches running into it that show those processes which must be done before it can be started.

It is easily seen that for building a submarine this graph will involve very many nodes and branches. Indeed, as with a flowchart, there is not a single final level of detail, merely levels of detail that serve various purposes. Thus the processes (lines connecting nodes) in one PERT chart can often be expanded into sub-PERT charts showing more detail. For example, the assembly of a motor can become a chart showing the sequence necessary in the assembly process for making the motor.

The next step is to get reliable estimates of the *time* necessary to carry out each process that appears as a branch of the graph. These times must be estimated accurately. Some very elaborate PERT chart methods also use the variability of the estimate, but for simplicity we shall omit this refinement. Thus a PERT chart has numbered nodes and numbers (time estimates for the process) associated with each line in the chart. With this information supplied to the computer in the form of tables, together with the target date for final completion (which is the final node of the graph), the computer can look back from the final node to the immediately preceding nodes and from the time estimates of the corresponding processes assign the date at which each of these earlier nodes must be completed. These nodes can be "backed up" in turn to their preceding nodes. If, as often happens, two or more branches go back to the same node, then the branch having the earliest time is used to assign the time at which this node must be reached if the entire project is to be completed on time. Thus the time to be associated with any node can be found (once all those nodes which depend on it have their times assigned) by picking the earliest time that is required. Continuing this way, the entire graph is filled in with the times the nodes must be reached if the whole project is to be completed on time.

Furthermore, the limiting critical path, or paths in case there are more than one, is marked. This critical path is the one that requires the longest time to traverse, and hence if any process on this path is lengthened then the entire program will require more time. This critical path gives management the information about where in the total project to watch most closely and shows how to monitor the whole project. Management must check that the nodes on the critical path are met on time, while other nodes can be allowed to slip a bit if necessary to ensure that the critical path is not delayed.

The effect of having management watch the critical path is, of course, that the critical path tends to get speeded up while other parts get slowed down. At regular intervals, daily or weekly, depending on the pace of the job, the already completed dates are entered and old parts of the chart are dropped. Also, because of early preparation for some of the branches on the critical path, and possibly others, the time estimates for various processes may become shorter or longer than originally estimated, and this will require that the critical path be recomputed. The new critical path will refocus management's view of what to watch, and the interplay of changing charts and management's attention keeps the pressure on just about where it is most needed. Thus there is a strong tendency for the whole project to proceed faster than it would otherwise, and the completion date gradually moves up. This simple decision device, the finding of the critical path by a computer (it can be done by hand, but machine results seem to have more authority), and regularly redoing the search for the critical path each time there is revised information and estimates, has proved to be a very effective tool of management for some types of projects. To the outsider it may sound idiotically simple, but it has proved to be a powerful tool for the management of complex, interrelated projects.

How is the program for the computer organized? Clearly, it needs to find a node with no time yet associated with it, and examine, from a table of lines, all outgoing lines. When a node is found that has all its successor nodes with times assigned, it is an easy matter to take the time associated with each node and combine it with the time of the corresponding line to get a list of times for the original node. The earliest time in this list (and where it came from) is then recorded.

An Example of the PERT Chart

Suppose we are given a number of activities, A,B, ... ,M with the corresponding times to complete them, together with precedence relations among them:

1. *A* and *B* are initial, independent activities which may be concurrent; *A* is of duration 3 (units of time: hours, days, or weeks) and *B* is of duration 2.

2. *C* (of duration 6) and *D* (duration 3) cannot start before *A* is finished.

3. *E* (duration 4) cannot start until *B* is finished.

4. *F* (duration 1) cannot start until *A* and *B* are finished.

5. *G* (duration 1) cannot start until *D* and *F* are finished.

6. *H* (duration 2) cannot start until *E* is finished.

7. *J* (duration 10) cannot start until *A* is finished.

8. *K* (duration 4) cannot start until *C* and *G* are finished.

9. *L* (duration 1) cannot start until *C*, *G*, and *H* are finished.

10. *M* is the final activity (duration 6) and cannot start until *J*, *K*, and *L* are finished.

a)

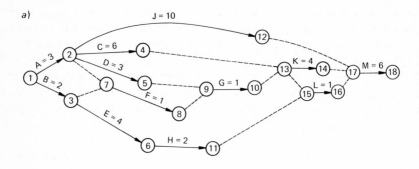

b)

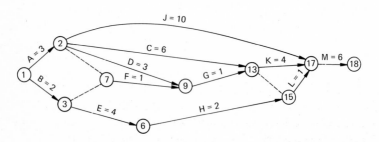

Figure 12-2

We try making a sketch using numbered nodes. Start at the node on the left and end at the node on the right (Figure 12-2*a*). The chart can then be consolidated a bit (Figure 12-2*b*).

We can now tabulate the information in sorted order in the *activity* column of Table 12.1-1.

Step 1. Reckoning time backward from node 18, node 17 must be at time 6, which is found by scanning the second index of the activity column for the active time node 18, time 0 and activating node 17 at time 6, also killing the active status of node 18.

Step 2. The active node 17 activates 15 at time 7, node 13 at time 10, and node 2 at time 16.

Table 12.1-1

	activity	duration	times	max. time	sequence
A	1-2	3			
B	1-3	2			
	2-7	0	12		
D	2-9	3			
C	2-13	6	16		Step 4
J	2-17	10	16		Step 2
E	3-6	4	13		Step 4
	3-7	0	12		
H	6-15	2	9		Step 3
F	7-9	1	12		
G	9-13	1	11		Step 4
	13-15	0	7	10	Step 3
K	13-17	4	10		Step 2
L	15-17	1	7	7	Step 2
M	17-18	6	6	6	Step 1

Step 3. Node 15 has only one "backup" source. It is activated at time 7. It backs up (searching right hand index for 15s) node 13 to time 7 and node 6 to time 13.

Step 4. Node 13 is now filled, and the maximum time is 10, so node 13 is backed up to node 9, time 11, node 2 to time 16. But node 6 was also filled in step 3 with maximum time 9, so it too is backed up giving node 3, time 13.

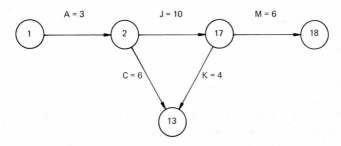

Figure 12-3

Table 12.1-2

activity		duration	times	max. time
A	1-2	3	$\underline{19}$	$\underline{19}$
B	1-3	2	15	
	2-7	0	12	
D	2-9	3	14	$\underline{16}$
C	2-13	6	16	
J	2-17	10	$\underline{16}$	
E	3-6	4	13	13
	3-7	0	12	
H	6-15	2	9	9
F	7-9	1	12	12
G	9-13	1	11	11
	13-15	0	7	$\underline{10}$
K	13-17	4	$\underline{10}$	
L	15-17	1	7	7
M	17-18	6	$\underline{6}$	$\underline{6}$

We now have active nodes 9, 7, and 3 to back up. We get, when all is done, Table 12.1-2, where the underlined times show the two critical paths.

From this it should be an easy step to prepare a flowchart, or a program outline, for doing the PERT chart on a computing machine. As usual, we ignore the final details of the programming process.

OPTIMIZATION   **12.2**

We have repeatedly emphasized the growing importance of simulations in our attempts to understand the complexity of the world that daily faces us. Many of the simulations involve the extensive use of a computer. Behind most simulations is the desire not only to simulate what is happening but to see how to alter things to get a better result. The quantities that we may regard as being under our control to alter as we please we will call *the parameters of the problem*. Thus the question being asked is how to alter the parameters from where they are now, or in a new situation, how to initially select them, so that we get the best result. "Best" must be explicitly described if the computer is to be used to find it.

It is a common experience that the simulation part of the computer program, hard as it may be to get the facts and write out the details, is often much easier than is the optimization part. If there is only one parameter to be varied in our search for the optimum, then a simple search process might be organized as follows:

Make a small change in the parameter and see if this improves the result. If it does, then try another change in the same direction. If the step did not improve the result, try a step in the opposite direction. Continue taking small steps in the direction of improvement until you find a local optimum where steps in either direction degrade the result.

When there are a few parameters in the problem, then such elementary methods can be used. But when the problem becomes complex it is necessary to develop more sophisticated methods for optimizing the design of a system.

It should be evident that what we found by the above method was a local optimum, and that better values might possibly be found far away from where we were searching. This is a sad fact of life, and not much can be done about it in practice except to try to use some imagination about where we search.

The field of optimization has a long history, but the appearance of computers and their power of simulation has led to a greatly increased interest in the methods used, and consequently to the development of a comparatively new discipline called *optimization theory*.

Unconstrained Optima

The simplest optimization problems (to find a maximum or a minimum) are those that have no restrictions (constraints) on the parameter values that may be used. Such problems may be likened to hill climbing (for a maximum) or hill descending (for a minimum). We imagine that we are climbing a hill and that all we can see is the local topography of the hill. The obvious strategy is to always walk in the direction of rising ground. Indeed, if we were in a hurry we would always take a step in the direction of greatest local slope. This local strategy does not guarantee that we will get to the top along the shortest path—counter examples are easy to construct—but it seems to be better than any other simple strategy that makes use of only local information.

Will we get to the highest point? We will get to a local highest point from which we cannot take a step to a locally higher point. If we are determined to find the highest point, we can try starting out at a number of various places and each time climbing to a local peak. Note that each attempt will cost us time and money, and that we simply cannot try *all* possible starting points. When we follow this strategy we run the risk that there is a *needle rock* that has a very small base and that rises higher than any other hill. If the base is very narrow, we will have a very small chance of ever starting on the needle and being led to the top.

How, using a computer, do we find the direction in which the hill is rising? We can try a random step to see if, using the simulation, the step improves matters or not, but experience shows that random trials are apt to be very expensive. There are many ways of searching for the next trial, based mainly on the last few steps. It is important to realize that we need not take exactly the steepest ascent. It may be so expensive to find it that we will settle for a relatively good step. We will still get to the same hill top, probably ("probably" because it is possible that we will occasionally slip through a pass and onto another hill in one of the searches and not in the other).

It should be clear that the computer plays an essential role in this process because it runs a complete simulation at every step to see if matters have improved or not. Thus the simulation program supplies the number for making the decision that progress was or was not made by the proposed step. That is where the machine time goes. The part of trying to figure out what step to take next often consumes very little machine time, but the method of search, if it is inefficient, can cause so many steps to be taken that the optimization cannot be carried out in practice. Thus the details of the method of optimization are very important, though they take little time to execute on the machine.

Constrained Optima

In many problems there are constraints on the values of the parameters that we may use. Thus it is not possible to manufacture a negative number of items, the city budget will not allow expenditures of more than a given amount in any one month, or the strength of a steel beam cannot be taken to be more than a certain amount.

These constraints can be viewed as *fences* on the hill we are climbing, fences that we may not climb over. It will be immediately clear that we will occasionally find that we are trapped in a local position where the ground rises but the fence, or fences, block us, and that we will have to descend a bit and try climbing from some other place. This complicates our search a great deal.

It is a plausible strategy to try climbing until you run into a fence and then follow the fence as long as it goes in the direction of the steepest ascent that you are allowed by the fences. If the fence wanders off in a downward direction you would, of course, ignore it, but in practice this rarely happens. Thus in constrained searches for an optima, there is a great deal of "walking along a fence," and the methods of incorporating this into the search strategy are numerous.

In the very simplest cases, where the fences are all straight lines and the hill being climbed is nicely shaped, we can give guaranteed, reliable, efficient methods. In complicated cases we have to run the simulation many times and in the end we have only a local optimum.

In the absence of known strategies of searching we often resort to plausible actions, called *heuristics*. These strategies are not guaranteed to work, they are only plausible. But this is what we as individuals so often do in our daily lives: we do what seems reasonable. This heuristic approach to optimization and to decisions will be discussed further in Chapter 14 under the more glamorous title of "Artificial Intelligence."

SUMMARY 12.3

The impressive word *decision* here means no more than putting a different address in the location that has the address of the next instruction. It is the enormous number of elementary decisions that gives the illusion of a profound decision. Thus the PERT chart gives valuable results, though it is essentially a simple tool for management.

Decisions are based on many things: known facts, likely things to do, and even on statistical results. The latter are often thought to have greater reliability than they possess just because a large computer does them and they are printed out so neatly.

CHAPTER 13

IBM 702 Electronic Data Processing Machine (1954)
Courtesy of IBM Corporation.

13

The Economics of Computers

The economics of computers is a large and complex subject. In order to organize our approach to the topic we shall work from the outside in, from the largest view to the most local—from macro- to microeconomics. Thus we shall look in turn at the computer industry as a whole, both hardware and software, then at the computer itself, both as seen from the outside and from the inside of the machine, then at how humans try to use and organize machines, and finally at some of the implications of present trends.

Economics has been called "the dismal science," and most people find it uninteresting *except* when the results affect them—and then they holler when it is too late!

THE COMPUTER INDUSTRY AS A WHOLE   13.1

The computer industry has grown from almost nothing in 1950 to an estimated value of $18 billion in 1970 for installed general-purpose business and scientific computers. The current growth rate of sales suggests a doubling period in sales of approximately three years.

The growth in dollar value corresponds to the growth in the number of machines in use. While the biggest computers get more expensive each year, the small ones get cheaper, so the average cost of machines does not change as much as one might expect. Thus in 1967 there were about 30,000 computers installed, and in 1970 an estimated 60,000 or more.

In the present organization of the computer industry a few manufacturers, perhaps 10 in all, make most of the computers, with one, IBM, having around 70 percent of the market, year in and year out. In the past, the manufacturer of the computer supplied most of the peripheral equipment and software that the user needed, but this is rapidly being changed as software houses and components industries spring up almost daily. This is due partly to the government insistence on "plug-to-plug compatibility" and the so-called unbundling ruling which is forcing separate charges for hardware and software rather than letting the manufacturer market them both without indicating the costs of the separate items.

It would appear that in time the software industry may exceed the hardware industry in dollars spent by the user. One can sell a new machine once, and perhaps resell it once or twice more as secondhand, but the need for software goes on all during the life of the machine so that there can be a potentially greater market for software. On the other side, however, the cost of making another copy of a computer is high even under mass production methods, while the cost of making another copy of some software is relatively little.

There is a growing market for peripheral equipment like digital-to-analog converters, teletypewriter equipment, display devices, remote input devices, plotting boards, microfilm outputs, special printers, special sensing equipment, optical readers, etc. As we learn to use the computer in more situations we need more kinds of equipment to provide the interface between the computer and the real world.

The computer industry has required a rapid growth in both capital investment and people employed in the industry. Thus any way you look at the computer industry it is at present a "growth industry," and it is hard to believe that it will not continue to be one for some years to come. However, foreseen and unforeseen technical developments may alter these two aspects of the industry, and in the far future both the capital and human investments necessary to keep up with the indicated growth demands may not be so great as many people seem to believe.

THE EXTERNAL ECONOMY OF COMPUTERS 13.2

Computers are usually acquired in the belief that they will save money by doing some particular job more cheaply, but all too often this hope is not (apparently) realized. Instead, the great capacity of the machine is used to do (1) much more of the old things such as report production and handling more employees' checks and more sales, and (2) new things that were not contemplated at the time that the machine was planned for and acquired. This has certainly been the history of machines in the past. Presumably as society gains more experience with computers, users will more accurately judge what to do with them, but at present we are far from that day.

While the anticipated direct savings from getting a computer are often not realized, the indirect savings and the doing of new things have made machines a great asset, so much so that in many areas a company without a lot of computing capacity is at a great disadvantage and in some areas cannot compete at all. Once upon a time, getting a machine was a prestige symbol. Now it tends to be a necessity if one is to stay in business. In our dynamic, changing society either a company moves agressively forward or it soon dies. Because of their innate flexibility, computers are one of the better tools for handling changes and keeping up with the inevitable march of progress (in a technological sense).

INTERNAL ECONOMY OF COMPUTERS 13.3

The first computers were designed to pass everything through the accumulator. Thus in the processes of reading in and printing out, the information passed directly, word for word, through the accumulator, and as a result tended to tie up the central processing unit (CPU) during these relatively slow processes. Furthermore, many of the other things that the machine did happened in the accumulator so that only one thing could be done at one time.

It was soon realized that this was not an efficient way to run a large, expensive machine, and the designers gradually put in, here and there, small special control units to carry out special processes. Thus the modern computer has its input and output almost completely buffered, meaning that the central processing unit can do further calculations while the machine is reading in and out.

Special devices such as index registers (which are really special fixed-point adders) are another way of increasing the speed of the machine. Many other features that allow some degree of parallel processing are available, such as an instruction overlap that permits decoding of the next instruction while the previous one is being executed.

Thus, while the classical picture of the computer shows a single central control, in fact, a computer is much more likely to be a central processing unit with a number of satellite processors that are driven by the central control and report back to it. This clearly results in a higher initial cost, but also in a greater relative increase in computing capacity.

Some overlap of operations may also be accomplished by means of elaborate software systems, as well as extensive use of the buffering to adjust the very fast speed of the central processing unit to the relatively slower input, output, and backup stores.

Thus, in this view, much of the change in the design and use of computers has been in response to the obvious efficiency of *parallel processing* as against the strictly *serial processing* of the earliest machines.

TIME SHARING FOR HUMAN COMPUTING
IN REAL TIME   13.4

The current trend in the use of computers involves a number of separate ideas, all of which are designed in one way or another to give the user better service. Thus the economics of the human user are beginning to get priority over the economics of the computer itself.

The first idea (publicly demonstrated originally in 1940 at the Dartmouth meeting of the American Mathematical Society) is the *remote console*, at which the user can sit and apparently have control of the remote computer. (In the demonstration the computer was in New York City.) Most often this remote console is a simple variant of a typewriter, a teletypewriter, or similar equipment, all of which have the difficulty of being able to print, at most, around 10 or 15 characters per second. A few remote consoles have a television screen (also called a cathode ray tube, or CRT), but these require more expensive communication links to the computer.

The second idea is *time sharing*. The remote typewriter wastes a great deal of the machine time if it has complete control of the computer, because of, among other reasons, the slowness of the input and the output. One simple method of time sharing is to give each of, say, 100 remote typewriters a *time slice* of 1/100 of each second. A *monitor program* at the main machine starts work on your problem by loading up all that you have stored in the backup memory into the main memory and resuming the work where it left off. It works on your problem until the time (1/100 of a second) is up. The monitor program (activated by a real-time interrupt from a clock) then puts your problem back into the large backup store and picks up the next person's problem. Thus each person has all of the main machine, except for the small monitor program space, almost 1/100 of the time, so that it appears to each person as if the machine were 1/100 as fast as it actually is. Such a system needs a buffer store (1) to accumulate the inputs, since they come in at the random times of the typewriter key strokes during the interval of one second, and (2) to fill up the output buffer to keep the various typewriters going between the times that they are connected to the machine. Of course, when there are not 100 people wanting service during the same second, then the system can either give faster service, going to the next active problem, each for 1/100 of a second, or else making the length of time given to the individual problem a bit longer.

Time sharing by time slicing is easy to organize. Its great asset is that it is easy to arrange that the monitor program is stored with machine interlocks so that whatever your program may do it cannot get at the monitor program and destroy it. Thus troubles in a single problem cannot get over into other problems. Its greatest weakness is that only comparatively simple problems can be handled by the system.

Time sharing is very popular because it greatly increases the efficiency of the human user at only a moderate loss of machine efficiency.

The idea of *multiprogramming* is a variant of time sharing by time slicing. In multiprogramming more than one program is in storage at one time, and the switching from problem to problem depends on what goes on in the problem itself. Thus if a problem calls for something that is going to take a good deal of time (by machine standards of speed), such as reading from some slow device, the monitor switches to the next problem automatically. Multiprogramming is mainly used for machine efficiency. It avoids the wasted time to bring in and take out a complete program each time the control switches to the next problem. It also avoids the delays that occur when slower parts of the machine are used, by overlapping the operations. But one of the costs is that any particular program does not have a definite place in storage. It may appear at various times in various places in storage, depending upon what is in storage when it is being brought in. Another cost is that there is a great deal of overhead in the planning to bring up or put back into slower storage the various parts of the various problems that are being worked on at the same time. There is also the very serious problem of the protection, not only of the fixed monitor system, but also of other people's problems, from troubles that may occur in any one particular problem. Still another cost is the vexing fact that a single machine failure may now involve many different people.

The idea of *multiprocessing* is a still further refinement. In a multiprocessing computer there are several similar processors working on various problems at the same time. Again this idea is designed to improve the machine efficiency. It has the nice feature that if one processor goes down due to a failure of some kind, it can be taken out of service while the other processors continue to work. As a result, when a failure occurs the user sees at most a slightly degraded quality of service, and not a complete stoppage as on a uniprocessor system. Unfortunately, the problems of building a multiprocessing, multiprogramming, time-sharing system are more difficult than is usually believed, and so far only partial successes have been achieved, although there appears to be no inherent reason why such convenient, efficient machine systems will not be available in the future. On the other hand, the economics of the heavy overhead on such a complex system may limit its development in many areas.

The huge size of the investment in money and effort, and the apparently inherent advantages of large complexly organized computers over small simple ones, leads to the idea of a *public computing utility* which we will discuss later.

Typical Time-sharing Systems Available

The great interest in time-sharing systems has led a number of companies, both big and small, to offer time sharing on a computer via a remote console, usually a teletypewriter. The user sits at his console and dials a telephone connection to the computer, and when things are set up properly he is ready to use the computer. Whenever he wants a few moments time he gets it almost immediately, and whenever he wants to pause or stop, then his problem is automatically put into the backup store of the computing facility. Thus at his convenience he has almost direct access to the computer.

The cost is surprisingly low. Typically the cost of the rented telephone lines (which at present are charged for the duration of the call and not for the few moments of actual data transfer) is about equal to the cost for the main-frame time of the computer (which is charged only for the few seconds of use). Of course, there is a wide variation in the two costs, but they tend, over a period of time, to be approximately comparable.

Time sharing has proved to be a great help to people with small problems who could not afford the cost of maintaining a large machine, or even the know-how to run one directly. In large laboratories which have access to large machines, the remote typewriter for small problems is also very popular, and some well-known people in the computing field have had consoles installed at home in their basements or even in their bedrooms! Thus they are free to work at odd hours and can have the quiet of home rather than the noise and interruptions of the typical office environment.

A typical time-sharing central computer and its peripheral equipment can be purchased for around $1 million, or rented for approximately 1/40 as much per month. The economics of the situation has encouraged a number of groups to form small companies and to start a time-sharing service in their locality. There are many problems in doing this, and figures are not publicly available to be sure, but it is strongly suspected that they have not proved to be very profitable so far. It has been predicted that by 1980 there may be 3 million remote typewriter-like consoles, which should indicate the popularity of time sharing. Presumably it will become an economically viable industry, but the impact of the minicomputers is yet to be understood. These may provide an alternate approach to the problem of efficient use of humans in the man-machine complex.

THE IDEA OF A PUBLIC COMPUTING UTILITY   13.5

Time-sharing systems that are generally available when you want them, but for which you don't pay when you don't want them, suggest the idea of a *public computing utility* similar to electric utilities. In the electric utility you have a plug in your wall that you can use as you please, provided you meet some reasonable requirements. You can use the electric power to light your house, cook your roast, heat your oven, run a fan or an air conditioner, operate your power tools, and so on. The utility offers you the electric power and charges you (beyond a certain fixed minimum amount) according to the amount of power you use and not for how you use it.

A computing utility would similarly provide a plug in your house, or office, which would connect you to a large computing capacity, and you would again be charged a flat minimum fee plus only that amount which you use and without regard to what you compute.

To demonstrate these ideas, some years ago a modified portable electric typewriter was exhibited at computer meetings. It had an attachment so it could be connected to the standard telephone and to the computer. When this was done the typewriter and the computer could communicate by tones or beeps. Such devices are now commercially available.

This suggests such applications as a traveling salesman for a company sending in his orders and reports for the day. Similarly, a field engineer could send in the details of something he wants to build and get back estimates of the costs and time to do the job. Of course, this would use the company's private formulas. As a result, the next day the client could be given a firm bid on his proposal.

A public utility that supplied readily available and cheap computing would give rise to many new uses of computers. At present, imagination is almost the only limitation on what could be done.

THE IDEA OF AN INFORMATION UTILITY   13.6

Similar, and closely related to the public computing utility, is the idea of an information utility which would, through the use of computers, supply useful information upon request. Not only could the computer locate relevant formulas and figures as well as compute the appropriate answers, but in principle any written textual material could be available. As an example, the contents of the Encyclopedia Britannica could be stored in the machine and the user could, via a suitable form of index, locate the material he wanted to have. A reasonable amount of querying and searching via the local typewriter would probably be necessary before the complete article was typed out on the remote console (or delivered in some other manner). Often the complete article would be too long and some searching for the paragraphs of interest for the specific request would be necessary before the information was sent.

Business record files, especially credit bureau records, are already in the headlines, along with various governmental files.

The idea of a public information utility, although very charming, has a great many hidden problems. As one simple one, if a book were stored in the computer, how would we pay the usual royalties that are currently due to the author when his book is sold and which to some extent motivates him to write the book in the first place? (This rule of royalties is being violated everyday with the aid of photocopying machines, so perhaps it is not serious in the sense that the author can be ignored in the short run. But it will be serious in the long run because many potential authors will in turn ignore the hard work of developing, organizing, and selecting the material in the first place.)

Perhaps the main problem of a public information utility is the assignment of responsibility for the accuracy, reliability, and completeness of the information files. A "user beware" system is *not* satisfactory. The power to alter some types of information that is stored in the file is clearly something that must also be watched carefully. The average reader probably already has his own ideas of what should and what should not be done in these matters.

There appears to be no end to the dreams people have in this matter of information storage and retrieval via computers and remote consoles. For example, the whole of the university card catalog as well as the library itself could be stored (just how is never stated) so that you could get at many short references via your typewriter, and the longer ones could be sent to you via the mail. Often it is supposed that you will have a television screen, and you can view the material directly rather than via the slow typewriter, and with your own private photocopier you can make copies for more detailed studies. Where dreams and wishful thinking begin and reality ends is hard to know at this moment.

COMPUTER UTILITY REGULATION   13.7

As with any public utility there is the problem of the control of that utility. In the absence of any governmental action, many small computer companies are being formed, both good and bad, and it is to be expected that in the normal course of economic evolution various mergers will produce a number of big computer utilities. When and how the government will step in and with what regulations on what may and may not be done, remains to be seen, but it seems very unlikely that the computer utilities will be allowed to flourish totally unregulated. Computing capacity and the ability to recover information and process it is so very important in our current civilization that it can give to the unscrupulous expert far too much power.

Thus the computer utility concept, which has its basis in the economics of using expensive computers, data, and processes when needed, in a time-sharing mode, and not paying for them when you don't, leads gradually to very hard, but important decisions to be made about public control of such power. And this is only one more example of the fact that the average person in this country must sooner or later make up his mind as to what he wants his civilization to be and what he does not want it to be, so that when he gets his turn to vote he will vote according to his *enlightened self-interest*.

UNEMPLOYMENT   13.8

There are two schools of thought about what impact computers will have on our employment patterns. The first school, to which many computing experts belong, believes that machines can make simple decisions (Chapter 12) that are reliable, accurate, fast, unprejudiced (in a very real sense), and so are desirable for many functions in our society which are now performed by unskilled labor of one form or another. To put it bluntly, people who are now getting paid for what amounts to little more than doing simple, "conditioned responses" will inevitably be put out of work by a machine. The machine requires less personal attention, is not so apt to go on sick leave, nor strike, nor require old age pensions, nor cause personal squabbles with other employees. It will do as it is told and not "goof off" or do the wrong things because it forgot, and so on. The argument is that simple economic facts cause machines to be used to displace the low-intellectual-level worker in many jobs.

Some people claim that the automation of factories and other production facilities, like computer controlled chemical plants, has already done this. The computer not only does a cheaper and more satisfactory job than did the human, but because of its inherent reliability and accuracy it permits a much better product to be built. Indeed, one of the main effects of automation with a digital computer is to make possible a high quality product that simply could not be produced by the old-fashioned human controls. These are some of the forces moving us toward a machine controlled basis for material production.

The second school, to which many people in labor unions, the U.S. Bureau of Labor Statistics, economists, etc., tend to belong, believes that this picture is the result of naive thinking by people who simply do not understand the economic system. They point out all the jobs that the huge new computer industry has created and all the new services that it now produces for humans to consume, and they claim that this more than compensates for the job losses. They claim that it is mere job displacement that has been going on for centuries.

These two views are not completely contradictory, they differ on where the stress is put. But where does the truth lie? If it were easy to answer, there would not be arguments between the two schools.

If one attempts to look at what happens when a computer is installed to save some money and jobs, what does one typically see? Consider the registrar's office at a university where I recently taught. When the computer was first brought into the registration and record keeping business, a great deal of money was involved in getting the machine and developing the software. One would naturally expect that when the system was finally going, the registrar's office would have a lot fewer people. But what does one apparently find? Nothing of the kind! When the question is asked, "How can it be economical to install machines to do what was being done by hand and then find the same number of humans still employed?" it is natural to further ask, "How can this be? What is paying for the machine itself?" The answer seems to lie in the fact that the records are more efficiently kept and that this efficiency is translated not into the displacement of humans, but into more of the old services plus a number of new services, as well as a better quality of service.

Sometimes a computer installation does displace jobs, and fewer persons are on the company payroll, but quite often there has been only a displacement and rearrangement of jobs, and the increased power in production is consumed in greater and better output, and not in layoffs. However, this change has required an "upgrading" of many people. It is this aspect of the situation that the computer expert school tends to emphasize.

It would be nice to have some national figures on the whole matter, but it is practically impossible at this time to get anything that is meaningful and which will convince those on either side that they are wrong. There is little question that there are job changes, but that has been with us throughout this century, though it has been going on at an increasing pace. What is being asked is the effect of computers on the *net* employment. The size of the new job pool created directly by computers plus the new jobs that are created indirectly by computing machines is so large and uncertain on the one side, and the job losses so hard to be certain of on the other, that the net change will be the difference of two large, very uncertainly known (and to some extent always arbitrary) numbers. You can take your choice, and your choice will probably reflect your biases more than it will reflect any reasoned decisions.

The traditional economists regard the computer as a trivial change compared with the industrial revolution, which in the end created more jobs than it *apparently* displaced (but how would you prove this claim?). The computer experts claim that the traditionalists have no concept of what the modern computer can and will do in another 50 years, and that the traditionalists are sticking their heads in the sand. Certainly it is true that classical economic theory has no place in its many theories for the technologically new devices. Economic theory always seems to proceed in small extrapolation steps from the present, while new devices produce quantum jumps in our society.

What worries the computer experts, among other things, is that they will find themselves in somewhat the same position as the atomic scientists did: they will have created a monster over which they will in the end have no control and which they will often wish they had never created. While it is war and the destruction of lives, of property, and possibly of the whole civilization that worries the atomic scientists, it is the vast unemployment that will fall mainly on a single class of people, the poorly prepared, and will probably cause much misery, that worries the computer scientists. Furthermore, it is the fear that a monstrous society will result from the misuses of machines. These are emotional matters of such magnitude that it is very hard to think straight about the whole thing. Instead of careful thought and accurate data, both sides use slogans, emotional appeals, and threats. The person who tries to be objective and to find out the truth soon discovers that it is either very hard or even impossible to get reliable facts, that too many people are bent on proving their side of the argument. Even *Fortune* magazine, which usually seems to do a good job, went far astray, in this author's opinion, in a recent series of articles on the topic of computers and unemployment.

Thus, although economics is the dismal science, each adult in our society needs to make up his own mind about how much uncontrolled economics is to be allowed to influence the evolution of computers, and how much governmental regulation is to control. The topic may be dismal, the choice distressing, but it is an urgent one.

SUMMARY 13.9

There are many changes occuring in the way computers are organized and used. Most of them have a sound economic basis, either in trying to use the computer efficiently or else in using the human efficiently. But many of the changes and applications of computers bring with them significant effects on our society and the people need to have some realization of what can be done to avoid the worst effects while encouraging the better ones.

IBM System 370 (1970)
Courtesy of IBM Corporation.

14

Artificial Intelligence

WHAT IS MEANT BY ARTIFICIAL INTELLIGENCE?   14.1

The idea of intelligence is a general concept, and it is hard to define intelligence satisfactorily. Sooner or later in almost any extended discussion of computing machines, the question comes up of whether or not computing machines can act intelligently. Put more simply, "Can a machine think?" is a question that is commonly asked. How is such a question to be answered? Clearly we need a definition of intelligence or else a test to see if some process can produce results that require the use of intelligence. Many people will give a definition of intelligence such as "Something like Newton or Einstein did." By this definition (if it can be considered to be a definition), most people are not intelligent. This tends to make the proposed test rather inappropriate since a definition of intelligence that excludes most of us is hardly satisfactory.

If we are to proceed along the lines of testing whether or not a machine can think, it is necessary to frame a definition of *the least act*, or else something close to the least act, which, if done by a machine, would persuade you to accept the idea that machines have intelligence. How else could it be demonstrated fairly? But the more you consider the *least* act of intelligence, the more you are apt to become disenchanted with the idea, for the very approach seems to contain a contradiction. Either you have framed a task that is not minimal, or else so simple a task cannot be showing intelligence.

Let us be clear about it. If we are going to decide whether machines are capable of intelligence by judging only the output of a machine, then it appears to be necessary to have a statement that describes in sufficient detail what will be an acceptable proof so that we can examine the ouput of a machine. If the result is as agreed, we will say that machines can act intelligently.

There are, of course, other approaches to the question. One can say that intelligence is not to be judged by the output, but by the way it is done ("It ain't what you do, it's the way that you do it"). In this approach, a child may be using intelligence when he is multiplying two numbers together, while a machine which produces the same result is not using intelligence.

There is still another approach, which is to frame the definition so that the effect is to have thinking and intelligence a property of humans (and possibly a few other animals, depending on how charitable you feel at the moment) and not a property of machines. Of course, that settles the question the way you want it settled. This approach is widely used, and often some care is taken to disguise the intention behind the definition. But when analyzed the proposal amounts to prejudging the situation.

Without debating the rightness or wrongness of such a definition, it is easy to see that such a definition is apt to be rather sterile, while the opposite assumption, that machines *can* think and act in intelligent ways, is apt to be more fruitful. The latter approach immediately sets the task of producing programs *that think*.

Years ago there existed a somewhat similar situation in chemistry. It was then believed that only *life* could create "organic" compounds. Unfortunately for the theory, a number of organic compounds (including urea) were synthesized in a laboratory. Although up to now chemists have not yet created life in a test tube (let alone a full-scale human) most people have abandoned the "vitalistic" theory that chemistry in living materials has a fundamental difference from chemistry in the laboratory.

What is clear, and we shall later give a number of examples, is that many acts that were once thought to require thinking (whatever that is and whatever relation that has to intelligent behavior) are now being done by computing machines, and it seems very likely that as time goes on many more such acts will be done by machines.

Thus as a practical matter, we shall simply assume that of course machines can think and act intelligently, and then examine a few of the ways we have to go about trying to give actual demonstrations. We shall reject a vitalistic approach to thinking and intelligence.

THE NEED FOR MACHINE INTELLIGENCE 14.2

The need for complex behavior by machines is quite apparent in many cases. To take one simple example, consider the problems that will face those who will try to explore the surface of Mars. They will want to send machines to do the work, but the machines will inevitably face situations that were not foreseen by the planners back on Earth, and the round trip signalling time from Mars to Earth and back to Mars will run into quite a few minutes, during which disaster may face the exploring equipment. Thus it will be necessary to any sophisticated machine exploration to have a program in the local (on Mars) computer that is directing the equipment, a program which has the ability to make choices and call for actions in situations that have not all been carefully examined beforehand. We will want at least a low level of intelligence for the machines we send to Mars to explore and relay back their measured results.

Indeed, this is almost our definition of intelligent behavior: the ability to act in suitable ways when presented with a class of situations that have not been exhaustively analyzed in advance, but which require rather different combinations of responses if the result in many specific cases is to be acceptable.

While the example of the exploration of Mars may be rather dramatic, in increasingly many situations there are so many alternatives that we simply cannot program what to do in each case. There are also many situations in which for one reason or another there is not time for man to intervene. Missile interception is an example. Or it may be that the situation is under control much of the time during which no intervention by humans is needed, but when the occasional emergency occurs suddenly, it requires such fast response that it is impractical to keep a human on standby duty. Perhaps supersonic airplane flight may fall in this pattern (it has a lot of automatic control equipment built in).

There is also the further humane reason, namely, a job may be so dull that it is cruel to require humans to monitor what is going on (Charlie Chaplin's *Modern Times* dramatized the evils of dull routine work). One hopes and expects that many of the dull jobs of society will in time be taken over by machines.

GAME PLAYING   14.3

One of the easiest fields to which machine programs are applied, and which at the same time seems to require intelligence, is that of game playing. For our purposes there are two types of games, those like tic-tac-toe which have a known strategy that can be followed, and those like checkers and chess, which at present have no known, practical strategy of exactly what move to make next in every situation. The first type are hardly worth considering in examining the question of whether machines can or cannot think. The second is far more interesting, and quite early in the history of computing there were papers written about how to program a machine to play chess. The early attempts were not very successful, and only recently have there been reasonably effective programs. A. L. Samuel of IBM tried a serious attack on checkers, and managed to produce a program that at times has beaten some checker experts, and in any case certainly plays a better game than Samuel himself can.

What are we to say to this? We can deny that the game requires intelligence, but we will be doing violence to the idea of the common man who plays the game since he feels that he is thinking hard when he tries to beat his opponent.

The attraction of playing games on a computer is that there are such nice, clean-cut rules of play and such a clear recognition of a win that it does provide a good testing ground for ideas.

THEOREM PROVING   14.4

Another field that seems to require thinking or intelligence is mathematics, and in particular, theorem proving. The earliest attempts seem to have been directed toward proving theorems out of a classic work on the foundations of mathematics, *Mathematica Principia*, by Whitehead and Russell. It was early demonstrated that many of the theorems of the earliest parts could be proved by a machine. Indeed, for a while it became a bit of a race to see how fast a machine could prove the theorems. In the process, some new proofs were found, but no great new results.

A more appealing area for theorem proving is that of elementary geometry. Galertner wrote such a program, which was given the theorem, among others:

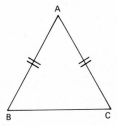

Given a triangle ABC with two sides AB = AC, prove that the base angles are equal.

To prove this theorem some people would bisect the base BC and draw the line to the vertex A, dividing the triangle into two triangles. Then they would prove the two triangles were congruent and argue that the corresponding angles were therefore equal. Other people would bisect the vertex angle A and likewise prove the two triangles congruent. But the machine printed out the proof:

Triangle ABC and triangle ACB are congruent, hence corresponding angles are equal.

The proof, while not actually new to mathematics, was not known to the men who wrote the program and came as a surprise to them. It has a certain mathematical elegance, and it appeals strongly to first-class mathematicians. Did, therefore, the machine exhibit creativity? Did it show originality?

LOGICAL AND PSYCHOLOGICAL NOVELTY   14.5

Not only the above examples, but many others illustrate that the man who writes a program is often surprised by the outcome—that in a limited sense the machine produces *novelty*. To make the matter clearer, let us distinguish between two types of novelty, *logical* and *psychological*. That the machines in the above examples exhibited psychological novelty seems beyond debate, but to those who program machines and believe that (unless the machine is malfunctioning) the machine does only what it is told to do, then it is not capable of logical novelty. This distinction seems worth making and to be a reasonable description of what we seem to believe.

Let us therefore examine just what psychological novelty implies before we dismiss it as trivial. Clearly chess will have only psychologically new moves, there are no logically new moves possible within the framwork of the game. Again, in mathematics, once the postulates (and definitions and theorems) are stated, then the proofs are only psychologically new, they are not logically new. Thus we should not underestimate how powerful and complex mere psychological novelty can be.

It is true that machines, when functioning properly, do what they are programmed to do. Even if we use random numbers to simulate random actions, they are still following out our instructions. What is not possible for humans to foresee is the complex consequences that arise from the interrelationships of the many simple parts with their simple choices and decisions. Indeed, that fact is where much of the charm of many games lies. The rules and the random distributions are all known (at least reasonably well) beforehand, but the shuffling of the cards, the play of the pieces, the turning of the wheel, or the roll of the dice, all produce results that are practically unforeseeable and which humans are often amused to see worked out. It is the "order of magnitude change" that produces the new effect.

SCHOOLS OF ARTIFICIAL INTELLIGENCE   14.6

There are a number of approaches to the general field of artificial intelligence. One school tries to duplicate human behavior and might be called the *robot school*. Another, for which the author feels more empathy, is more interested in using machines to *supplement human behavior*. The machine has such obvious advantages over humans in so many directions that it seems a shame not to combine our abilities with the machine's to produce a team that is more powerful than either one alone. To list a few of the advantages that are on the machine's side, first there is its blinding speed. Whereas humans signal through their nervous system at a few hundred meters per second at best, the signalling speed of machines is close to the velocity of light in a vacuum, namely, 186,000 miles per second. Second, there is their tremendous reliability. There is no question that a machine can do arithmetic and follow out simple instructions, one after another, far more accurately than humans can, no matter how hard humans try. In one second a machine can do more arithmetic than the average person will do in a lifetime, and so far as is known, no human ever did a full year of arithmetic without making a single mistake, yet machines usually get through a second safely. Third, there is the freedom from boredom that machines seem to exhibit while man is all too susceptible to it.

There are still other schools of artificial intelligence. One school tries to simulate small parts of the human nervous system, such as artificial neurons. Another tries to simulate gross behavior, such as having the machine produce an output much like that of a human when he is presented with a problem similar to the classic cannibals and the missionaries.

There is an amusing program which gives the illusion of acting like a psychoanalyst, another which answers a wide range of questions concerning baseball put to it (in slightly restricted English), and so it goes: many special programs appear on the surface to act intelligently.

CREATIVITY 14.7

We have tended more or less to equate intelligence and thinking and have occasionally slipped in the word originality. We shall now change a bit and use the word *creativity*. These ideas are all closely associated, so that since we apparently cannot actually define any one of them in a precise enough manner for testing on a machine, we will not bother to distinguish shades of meaning between them.

Creativity is a fancy word for a very common thing, *originality*. In women's clothes originality means *fashion*. It is something that almost everyone in our society wishes to have—he likes to feel that in some way he is unique. But, we agree that some people have it more than others. The margin between originality and crackpottery is as thin as that between genius and insanity is traditionally considered to be. The difference between fashion and bizarre clothes is likewise very little.

But creativity is something that our current culture puts great value on, regardless of whether that is wise or not. Until now theories of creativity (originality, or whatever you wish to call it) have necessarily been complex and beyond the hope of checking in detail. Now with the machine we have a chance to explore the question. If we have a detailed theory of what creativity is, then it can probably be simulated by a machine, or at least parts of it can, and the model can be tested out.

Such has been the approach in music composition, in theorem proving, and some other programs that fall in the field of artificial intelligence. The results to date seem, to this author at least, to show more where creativity is not than where it is. But that is the way most fields begin. There are many false starts, a few small gains, and a great deal of confusion. Sometimes this is followed by clarity, and sometimes not. But only where there is activity is there much hope for progress. Again, it is better to assume that machines can do it than it is to assume that they cannot: one leads to action, often foolish to be sure, but the other is apt to lead to nothing but a dead end.

Let us repeat the point. The machines *for the first time in human history* give us the power to explore the fascinating field of creativity. Given a detailed enough model it seems likely that we can simulate it, or part of it, on a machine to test out whether the model has any merit or not, and thus correct our errors and recognize our good guesses so that progress can be made.

STRATEGY TREES   14.8

Having examined the general situation, let us, as usual, take a more detailed look at some simple aspects of the problem to see in broad outline how it might be programmed on a machine. Consider, for example, a chess game (or checkers, if you prefer). Given a position of the pieces on the board and your turn to move, there are typically about ten moves to be considered, and for each move there are about ten moves the opponent may make. If we picture a tree-like structure where the nodes are board positions, and the branches are the possible moves leading to the new board positions, then we have a rapidly branching tree, where occasionally some branches come together.

If we look one full move ahead, your move followed by the opponent's move, then we want to find the move that leaves him the worst off. Suppose that we have a formula for evaluating how good a board position is (and this is roughly what a book on how to play chess tries to give, though usually in a sloppy, incomplete form). We assume first that when it is his move he will take the best of the moves available to him. For your move we want to choose the branch of the tree which keeps his best move as small as possible. Thus we scan each of the branches corresponding to your choices and for each branch find his best reply. Having found these numbers, we then want to minimize this, that is, we want to make the move that minimizes his maximum (best) reply to your move.

If we look two moves ahead, then we want to take alternate maximum, minimum, maximum, and minimum of the possible moves. But for the typical board position, there will be after two full sets of moves, about 10,000 positions to be considered, three moves ahead, 1,000,000 positions, and so on. Thus it is clear that we cannot, in fact, consider all possible alternatives very far before we will run out of computing time to do it.

And this is the typical situation in most complex problems related to artificial intelligence. The total number of alternatives available to us are far too many to be exhaustively considered. What we need to do is prune the tree of many of those branches that probably are of little use to us, without running too great a risk of losing those branches that will be more useful.

The concept of a *gambit* is the offering of what appears to be a loss at the moment, but due to the hidden interrelationships of the situation which we in our great wisdom have foreseen, and the opponent in his stupidity fails to see, will in the end mean our gain. These gambit moves will be lost unless the look ahead exceeds the recovery of the apparent loss. The more clever the gambit, the farther in the future is the hidden place where the recouping of the loss occurs. Thus a short look-ahead strategy will exclude the long gambit. But then, you can't have everything.

If we give up the idea of exploiting long gambits, we can proceed in the following fashion. Let us try first to find one good sequence of moves somehow. Having found the value of the board position at that point, we start the systematic search of the tree, and every time we start going down a branch along which we have already lost more than the one good move we have found, we abandon the whole part of the tree. Sometimes we will find a better sequence than the one we have, and when we do, we keep it as our reference and go on with our systematic search of the tree with this better way of pruning out the dead branches.

This is one way of pruning a tree. There are many other ways, and one of the central problems in artificial intelligence is how to prune away the probably bad branches without losing the better parts. Recently we have recognized that since our evaluation formula is only approximately right, it is worth putting some extra value on a branch that leads to many good moves, and tend to avoid those that lead to a single good move. Thus if later on our approximate evaluation formula turns out to be bad for some moves, we will still, at that time, have some other good moves to try. Similarly we can reverse the argument and favor those branches which seem to leave the opponent very few good moves.

The Eight Queens Problem

As a very simple case of tree pruning, consider the classic problem of placing eight queens on a chess board so that they cannot capture each other. This is the same as asking how to place eight pieces on the standard eight-by-eight board so that no two occur in the same row or in the same column and also no two on any one diagonal.

The number of positions to try is staggering. Blind trials would give $(64 \times 63 \times 62 \times 61 \times ... \times 57)/8!$ possible places to put the eight pieces (almost 3 billion). Instead of trying to produce this tree (the first point being the blank board, then 64 branches to the position with one piece on the board, then each such point having 63 branches to the board positions with two pieces on it, etc.), we proceed as follows to explore the entire board systematically.

We begin by numbering the board in the usual systematic fashion with the numbers 1,2, ... ,64. Then we try placing the first piece in position 1. Now we try the second piece in position 2. There is an

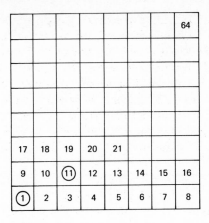

Figure 14-1

immediate conflict because there are two pieces in the same row, so that we can exclude all further placing of pieces and ignore all that part of the tree. Now we advance the second piece to square number 3, again fail, etc., until we get the second piece to square 11, where there is no conflict between the first two pieces. We thus have eliminated a large number of the possible positions with a few tries (Figure 14-1).

Now we try to place the third piece, starting with square 12 where there is an immediate conflict. Now we move the third piece forward through the numbered squares until we find a position where it neither conflicts with the first or second piece. Then we try to place the fourth piece, and so on.

Whenever we find that the piece we are trying to place has exhausted all possible positions, we set it aside for the moment and try advancing the immediately preceding piece, again searching for a square where it does not conflict with the still earlier pieces.

In this way we have a simple set of rules. Whenever we find a place to put the current piece we put it there and we start trying to place the next one, and whenever we find that we have run out of possible positions for placing the current piece, we drop back one and advance the immediately preceding piece one square and resume trying to place it so that no conflicts occur. Some thought will show that we will in time cover all possible successful positions (even the first piece will at times be advanced up to the eighth square, which is as far as we need to go—by symmetry we need only go to the fourth square) without actually looking at all possible placements and that there will be a very great reduction in the effort expended. Indeed, the proposed search strategy can be carried out completely by hand, though the human would notice a number of short cuts to speed it up still further.

An examination shows that this tree pruning is one in which we can be sure that we were not throwing away any solutions. Usually, as was observed in the previous section, we cannot find a completely safe pruning method, we can only find plausible methods of pruning. It is in this part of the problem that skill and insight into the nature of the problem help out so much: the human has to pick out the pruning method, and he faces the usual dilemma. Too little pruning and the tree will still be too big to explore, too severe pruning and the desired solutions may be lost.

PATTERN RECOGNITION   14.9

A standard type of question on IQ examinations is that of pattern recognition. You are given several cases and asked which of several possible items is the next case, that is, "What is the pattern of the objects that are given?"

Many problems in artificial intelligence fall into this category of pattern recognition. These problems are not only static, but dynamic. That is, one is asked to find a pattern among some processes, or within an ongoing process. Some of these pattern recognition problems can be cast as a tree exploration problem as in the last section, but some seem to be rather different.

One of the most studied pattern recognition problems is that of recognizing printed letters on paper. What with the varying type sizes and the small variations in ink and paper it is less easy than might be supposed. As a trivial example of the problems of reading a printed page, consider trying to find the size and level of the next line. Typically, one thinks that most of the letters lie between two imaginary lines with tails of some letters running below and the tops of some running above. If the first word of the next line were *gypsy*, the four out of five tails might start you out thinking that the lower line was in the wrong place and the size of type was bigger than it actually was.

Similarly, a run of letters with tops would make finding the upper line of the next line equally difficult. When further problems of skew and tilt are considered, it is easy to see that when the machine is not given all the details about size and type font and line spacing, it is a nontrivial problem to say exactly how one recognizes specific letters. In the recognition of handwriting problem, the variability makes the identification very much harder. Humans themselves in reading handwritten material usually have to use context and meaning as a basis for identifying many of the letters.

Even so simple a problem as recognizing human-sent Morse code turns out to be much harder than most people ever expect. The variations in the "fist" of even a single sender are much more than is usually recognized—at times his dashes may be shorter than were his dots at some other time in the same message.

The identification of blood samples and many other items such as particle tracks in high energy physics are other examples of pattern recognition. With some 40 million pictures of nuclear events taken in 1967, it is clear that machines do a great deal of the preliminary analysis of the photographs taken. Although pattern recognition in general is very hard, special cases have been handled and are used daily in many areas.

SUMMARY 14.10

We have examined only a few of the many examples of the use of machines to do "intelligent work." The field is rapidly advancing and has great possible usefulness in making life more pleasant for humans (by putting the routine, repetitive work on machines where it belongs). Many people, usually those who have had no real experience with the field, tend to fear the consequences of machines invading the domain of intelligent behavior. Undoubtedly machines will cause changes and job displacements, but that is one of the prices of change. It is not obvious that every change will be for the better, indeed some may cause great harm. It is up to humans to gradually learn and understand how to use artificial intelligence for human purposes, and to prevent its misuse. Blind opposition, ignorance, and fear are hardly sensible approaches to the field.

CHAPTER 15

In Retrospect

Let us look back and examine the material we have covered. After an introductory chapter giving some historical background and speculation on the origins of computing and computing machines, we examined the representation of information, then the representation of processes, and finally the computer itself as the machine that processes information. Thus we emphasized the basic truth that if a problem is to be done on a computer, it is necessary to represent the information in some suitable form, and to represent the processes to be applied to the information in some corresponding form. If these two crucial steps are possible, then in principle a machine can do the problem. If the two steps cannot be done, then there is no hope that a machine can do it. The practical, economic costs of the machine doing the job have been glossed over in the text, though obviously in practice the costs cannot be ignored.

The process of preparing a problem for machine computation is so simple in conception, and so difficult in practice *because of the necessity to supply every detail.* We have repeatedly illustrated this crucial step. In the chapters devoted to geometrical problems and business problems we considered mainly the processing of numbers, but we later went to nonnumeric problems such as the representation and processing of playing a game of three-dimensional tic-tac-toe.

Having covered the elements of computing, we turned to the main ideas needed in applications. Central to many uses are the ideas of a model and a simulation of a situation. We had to examine randomness and probability because they are involved in many applications of computers. We had to examine analog signals, the ideas of real time, feedback and stability because they are also fundamental to many applications.

We then turned to applications that are less definite and which have more socially important consequences: language, information retrieval, decisions, optimization of models and simulations, the always touchy subject of economics, and finally a glimpse at the fascinating area of artificial intelligence.

It has been a hasty trip and of necessity omitted a great deal. We probably omitted some things that will soon become important but are now not understood clearly. The trip began with the definite factual parts, passed briefly through a region of general, reasonably understood ideas, and ended with the frankly controversial parts. The chapters deliberately became shorter to leave room for discussion and thinking over what had been presented and what it might mean in the long run as we chose among alternate paths to the future. From the author's point of view the purpose of the book is (1) to provide a framework for thinking about how machines should be used in our society, and (2) to force the individual to come to his own conclusions as to how he should act when faced by machines and their consequences. It was not the intention of the author to force his prejudices on the reader, though he may have done so inadvertently.

The role of computers in our society will surely become larger and larger as the years pass, and it seems necessary that we have an enlightened populace in the voting booths if we are to have a pleasant future in a world of humans plus computing machines.

Index